Upgrade A-Level BIOLOGY

Glenn Toole

Vice Principal, Pendleton Sixth Form College, Salford

Susan Toole

Head of Biology, The Hulme Grammar School for Girls, Oldham

and former team leader and Examiner for A-level Biology

Stanley Thornes (Publishers) Ltd

First published in 1997 by:
Stanley Thornes (Publishers) Ltd
Ellenborough House
Wellington Street
CHELTENHAM GL50 1YW
England

A catalogue record for this book is available from the British Library.

ISBN 0-7487-2768-X

97 98 99 00 01 / 10 9 8 7 6 5 4 3 2 1

Artwork by Creative Associates
Typeset in Great Britain by Alden, Oxford, Didcot and Northampton
Printed and bound in Great Britain by Scotprint Ltd, Musselburgh, Scotland.

Acknowledgements
The publishers are grateful to copyright holders for granting permission for reproduction of copyright material on the following pages:

Phillip Allan Publishers: extracts from *Biological Sciences Review*
page 33 – Volume 6, No. 5 (May 1994); 'Genetically Engineered Plant Oils' by D Murphy

page 57 – Volume 8, No. 4 (March 1996); 'Chromosome Painting' by D Leggett

page 76 – *The Guardian*: extract from *The Guardian* 25 June 1996; 'What's That Lurking in the Fridge?' by Gail Vines

page 99 – *New Scientist*: extract from *New Scientist*, No. 2030 (May 1996) 'HIV Team Cracks Receptor Mystery' by Philip Cohen

page 123 – The Institute of Biology. Extract from the *Journal of the Institute of Biology*, Volume 43, No. 2; 'Biopharmaceuticals: Prospects for the Future' by Gary Walsh

CONTENTS

HOW TO USE THIS BOOK

You will, no doubt, have your own way of working through a book such as this and while we would not wish to prescribe too exactly how you should use *Upgrade Biology*, it has been written with a particular approach in mind. *Upgrade Biology* is essentially a companion to your textbook more specifically, but not exclusively, *Understanding Biology for Advanced Level*. While it can be especially helpful in the final weeks prior to a written examination, it will be most effective if used throughout your course, to test your knowledge and understanding of each topic as you learn it. Chapter 1 is, not surprisingly, the natural starting point, because mastering how to study effectively is an essential ingredient for success. Chapters 3–7 cover the five major themes of all Biology syllabuses. Each relevant chapter should be worked through as soon as your study of that particular theme has been completed.

We suggest the following format:
- *Revise the theme thoroughly* using the techniques perfected from reading Chapter 1.
- *Study the 'Topic Outlines'* from the relevant chapter. These provide a summary of the important issues and information for the theme.
- *Attempt the questions in 'Testing and Applying Knowledge'* Write down your answers to these short questions and then check your responses against the answers that follow. This will give you an indication of how much knowledge you have of the topics. We suggest that if you score anything less than 80%, you will need to re-visit your textbook to revise the subject matter more thoroughly. This revision could be selective – concentrating on the topics where you fared worst. Once this has been done you should try the questions again and repeat this sequence, until your score is in the range of 80–100%.
- *Read the 'Sample Question' and its 'Guided Response'* This is a typical type of examination question followed by a suggested answer that carefully leads you through how an accurate response can be constructed. You may like to attempt your own answer to the question first and then compare it with the response provided. Useful 'Tutorial Tips' are given alongside the answer to help you develop a good examination technique.
- *Attempt the 'Practice Questions'* that are characteristic of the types of questions set by all the major examination boards. Again 'Tutorial Tips' are provided to give you guidance when formulating your answer.

Once you have completed a question, check your response against the model answers that follow and award yourself a total mark. If you did not obtain full marks, try to identify where you went wrong and think about how you might improve in the future.
- *Study 'How to Approach Examinations and Modular Tests'* (Chapter 2) shortly before you sit each examination in order to acquaint yourself with the types of question you may encounter. Attempt past questions from the examination board whose papers you are sitting, putting into practice the advice provided in the chapter. In this way the techniques needed for success should come naturally to you on the big day and you will not need to spend precious time trying to remember them during the actual examination.
- *Study 'Guidance on Practical and Project work'* before embarking on either. Although this chapter has been placed at the end of the book, it is likely that you will need to study it early-on in your course as practical and theory work are inextricably linked and are therefore normally studied in parallel.

This last point illustrates the need to use the book flexibly. Although the content within each chapter has been logically arranged and is best studied in the order in which it is presented, the order in which different chapters are read will depend entirely on the sequence by which your particular syllabus is approached.

We hope you find *Upgrade Biology* useful and that it will make a contribution to your success in A-level biology. We wish you happy reading and good luck for the future.

Acknowledgements

The production of any book inevitably involves large numbers of people, without any one of whom its quality would be diminished. It is impossible to mention them all but we would like to give particular thanks to Margaret O'Gorman and Malcolm Tomlin at Stanley Thornes for their expertise, guidance and support, to our son David for the endless hours spent at the computer converting our scrawly writing and sketches into their present format, and to our other sons Andrew and Philip for their patience and enforced self-sufficiency.

PART 1

STUDY AND EXAMINATION SKILLS

1 HOW TO STUDY

So you have embarked on (or are about to) your A-level course in biology. What will it be like? How will it differ from your GCSE, or other previous experiences? What new skills do you need to develop in order to be successful?

Perhaps the most fundamental difference you will encounter at A-level is the greater range and detail of biological information that is required. Important skills for success are therefore the ability to access, understand and recall information and then be able to apply it to new situations and communicate your knowledge, ideas and thoughts in a clear and effective manner.

Let us be clear from the outset – there is no universal method of studying that can guarantee success or which suits everyone. We are all individuals with all the various differences that our genes and our environment have bestowed on us and a method of study that suits one person may prove totally ineffective for another. We do not seek to dictate how you should study, nor to suggest that one method is superior to another, but merely provide some ideas that you can experiment with. It is then up to you to select those methods that suit you best and that bring the most success.

Making notes

While for many students notes will be taken largely from lessons, lectures and textbooks, it is important not to underestimate the valuable contribution that can be made by notes from periodicals, television, films and radio. Whatever the source there are a number of ways in which note-taking can be made effective.

Distinguishing the important points

Most of what you hear, see or read as part of your study of biology will have some relevance. The problem is that there will rarely be time to write it all down. What is important, is for you to understand the main idea being put across and to note this down along with any supporting evidence. Try to appreciate the main theme of the lesson, article or programme; distinguishing this is easier said than done. The title may give some clue, although the increasing tendency for writers and programme-makers to compose a clever play on words sometimes obscures the nature of what follows. It is advisable to check with your tutor and other students in the early stages of your course, to ensure that you are on the right lines. Ask yourself whether the information given seems to support what you think is the main message – if not, you may be on the wrong lines so try an alternative one that fits the facts better.

Having decided what the theme is, keep relating the rest of the information to it. Learning a fresh topic can be like visiting a town for the first time – you may quickly become lost in the seemingly endless detail of the side streets unless you keep in sight some central, recognisable point that allows you to regain your bearings, and make sense of the pattern of the surroundings.

Having recorded the main points you will be able to fill in detail later. To do this, make sure you read over your notes as soon as possible after writing them, preferably the same day. In doing so add some of the detail you did not have time to write down at the time. Not only will revisiting your notes help you remember the information, it will allow you to seek clarification from your tutor or another source should you not understand everything you have written.

Writing your notes

While not everyone is capable of speed-writing, almost all of us can develop techniques that permit us to get down a considerable amount of information in a short time. These include:

- Writing in note form as grammatical prose is too time-consuming, e.g. 'Insulin from pancreas (islets of Langerhans β-cells) glucose $\rightarrow$ glycogen – stored in liver'.
- Using standard abbreviations of biological words, e.g. DNA, ATP, NADP.
- Using abbreviated forms of words, e.g. temp., sec, 2° (secondary).
- Developing your own shorthand, especially for commonly occurring biological words, e.g. P/S (photosynthesis), R/P (respiration). These must be restricted to your notes and not used in essays or examinations.
- Avoiding the use of rulers, coloured pencils, etc. unless essential for diagrams. Don't waste time underlining with a ruler or giving headings a different colour; it is more important to get down as much information as possible.
- Avoiding the use of correction fluid – if you make an error cross it out. Don't waste precious time using correction fluid and waiting for it to dry.

Organising your notes

Little is more daunting than page after page of unbroken prose. Imagine this book, or even this section, written as one long essay with no sub-sections or headings. Remember that when you come to revise you will probably not feel much like the task anyway. If you are then faced with a seemingly end-less collection of continuous notes you may well give up after a few minutes or even be put off starting altogether.

If possible try to devise a scheme of heading values, where there are three or four levels or sub-sections. An example is given below:

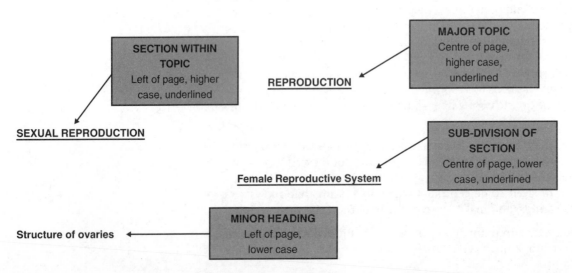

While this type of arrangement might seem unnecessary and time consuming, it will prove valuable when you want to quickly access information at a later date and help you divide your revision up into manageable portions.

Much of the hard work expended in writing and sub-dividing your notes will be wasted if they are not safely and logically stored. Hard back files with labelled cardboard dividers make access easier and saves time spent thumbing through a heap of jumbled papers for information on a particular topic.

An index at the start of each file is often useful, although page numbering is not essential as the addition of new material quickly makes this obsolete and necessitates renumbering. Essays on a topic can be added at the end of the relevant section of notes. Don't be afraid to reorganise your notes from time to time; it is not always desirable to keep them in chronological order. The order in which topics are taught may depend on many factors such as the seasonal availability of materials, the availability of apparatus and the preferences of your tutor. Be prepared to arrange your notes in the order that suits you best.

Adding to your notes

Notes should not be static, but dynamic, and constantly updated and adapted to suit your needs and those of the syllabus. As you pick up new information from books, television documentaries, science periodicals and newspapers add these to the relevant sections of your notes. Loose-leaf files are more or less essential for this purpose. It also helps to leave a number of lines at the end of each sub-section so that relevant information can be added at a later date. Always keep notes accessible and add new information immediately it comes to hand. It is good practice to keep the relevant notes at your side when reading a book or article on a particular topic. Adding material over the length of your course helps to keep you up-to-date. Remember that some notes will be nearly two years old by the time you sit the examination. In a subject that changes as rapidly as biology an awareness of recent developments is a distinct advantage.

Essay writing

Although essays are less common on A-level biology examination papers than they used to be, they are still commonly used during a course as a means of communicating ideas. They are especially useful because:

- There is scope for individual expression – there is not one correct answer, a whole variety of different responses can bring high marks.
- There is the opportunity to use the details and examples that have been acquired through additional reading.
- They allow a discussion of issues where there is conjecture and controversy rather than undisputed facts.
- They enable longer investigation of a topic to be made and time to develop logical reasoned arguments supported by evidence.
- Broad areas of biology can be explored.

Planning your essay

Having carefully read the essay title two or three times, jot down the ideas that immediately come to mind. Do not worry at this stage about organisation, simply note the key points as you think about them. Next read the parts of your notes, textbook and other books that relate to the essay, to generate new ideas. Make separate, more detailed notes from these sources that you think are important. Alternatively add page references to your plan. It is important to use a range of sources when researching essays. Essays are a valuable resource when it comes to revision. If they have been compiled solely from your own notes and the textbook they will contribute nothing original from which to revise. Think of essays not so much as a test of how much you have learnt, but rather as a means of expanding and varying your knowledge.

Having researched the essay take the plan and identify the important points that are central to answering the question. Mark them clearly. Try to arrange them in a logical sequence, so that the essay has a theme running through it. This is not always practical and, depending on the essay, it may be necessary to develop a number of separate lines of argument rather than follow a central theme. Where an essay involves two or more separate viewpoints it is important to establish a fair balance between each one.

Having determined the key points and arranged them logically, write them out in order, leaving a space between each. Now consider the peripheral material that you have amassed and try to associate it with one of the key areas listed. It may take the form of examples to illustrate a point, substantiating evidence to support an argument or simply additional detail to clarify an issue. Add concise notes to each of the key areas. If one or other area has no additional material added to it, it may be that further research is needed or possibly the point should be omitted altogether.

Writing your essay

It would be wrong to try to stereotype you into writing an essay in any particular way – style is very much an individual thing. There are, however, certain useful guidelines for you to follow:

- Keep the answer strictly relevant to the question asked. It pays to re-read the question from time to time to ensure this is being done.
- Make relevant points clearly and concisely.
- Support arguments with appropriate evidence.
- Use specific examples to illustrate points, giving the names of specific organisms where appropriate.
- Marshal ideas in a logical sequence.
- Write legibly and fluently, avoiding long, complex sentences that are hard to follow. Write grammatically correct sentences, not notes.
- Take care with spelling, especially over biological words, e.g. ileum (small intestine) and ilium (hip bone), carpal (wrist bone) and carpel (female part of flower), thymine (organic base in DNA) and thiamine (vitamin B).
- Unless specifically asked for, draw diagrams only if appropriate and where they make a useful contribution to the quality of the answer. Draw neatly – label and annotate.
- Avoid repeating points and do not fill out essays with superfluous or irrelevant material.
- Where an essay has a number of parts, distribute time in strict proportion to the mark allocation of each.

Illustrating your work

In addition to using words, ideas and information in biology are often communicated using tables, graphs and diagrams.

Tables and graphs

As a scientific subject biology involves data in many forms. You may be required to present data collected during an experiment or may be asked to analyse and interpret data that has been provided. It may be necessary at times to convert one form of data into another. The skill lies in choosing the most appropriate method for a given set of data. Use a table for numerical or brief written information. If you are writing long accounts in each section of the table, it is probably not the most appropriate way of presenting it. Remember to name each column and/or row clearly and where applicable give units e.g. time per sec, temperature per °C, rate per $mm^3 O_2 sec^{-1}$. When drawing graphs always:

- Give the graph a clear title, e.g. 'Graph to show photosynthesis in *Elodea*, measured in $mm^3 O_2$ released per second'.
- Choose scales so they are easy to use and make maximum use of the graph paper.
- Label axes clearly – state units and scale used.
- Plot points carefully (in pencil initially) using a dot surrounded by a circle or a small cross.
- Only draw the best straight line or a curve through the points where you have very good reason to think that the intermediate values fall on that curve. Where you do not know how the values vary between each plotted point, then join adjacent points with a straight line.
- If two or more lines are to be drawn on the same axes, distinguish each by clearly labelling them.

If using a histogram, bar chart or pie chart avoid excessive time-consuming shading. If it is necessary to distinguish one block from another, use cross-hatching rather than shading the entire area.

Diagrams and drawings

Care should be taken with all drawings, whether as part of your notes or in answering questions. Questions are more likely to ask you to label, annotate or interpret drawings rather than to construct them yourself. Unless a question specifically asks for a diagram consider whether using one is the quickest and most appropriate means of conveying the information. Advice on drawing diagrams is given in Chapter 8.

Reading and research

Reading as widely and as variedly as possible on biological topics is one way to increase your chance of a higher grade at A-level.

The problem is what to read? Magazines and newspapers often have articles of current biological interest especially on human related issues such as disease and pollution. While these articles do not always delve into detail or necessarily provide a balanced view they can help to keep you abreast of recent developments or stimulate an interest in new issues. Read them critically and use them as a source of ideas, arguments and up-to-date information.

Periodicals relevant to A-level biology include *Scientific American*, *New Scientist* and *Nature*, but perhaps the most relevant is *Biological Sciences Review*, a topical and interesting magazine written specifically for students of A-level biological subjects. All these contain a wealth of information on the latest discoveries and ideas. Many of the articles go beyond A-level and may be difficult to understand. It will not matter if the fine detail is incomprehensible provided the general principles are clear. Reading these periodicals is the best way of keeping up-to-date, and some notes, or at least a reference, should be added to the relevant section of your other notes.

Books remain the major source of biological information and are used for a number of purposes:

- As an aid to learning, helping you to recall factual information.
- For reference as a source of information for the writing of essays or for answering problems.
- As a means of improving understanding and providing a greater depth of knowledge.
- As a way of stimulating an interest in the subject.
- As a means of generating new ideas.
- For enjoyment.

The traditional large textbook is not intended to be read from beginning to end in sequence. Rather it should be used as a reference book, where specific pages or chapters are read in conjunction with the current topic being taught or the current week's essay question.

It is almost impossible to recommend to someone a biology book for general reading as so much depends on an individual's taste, not to mention the syllabus being studied. The best answer is to read, initially at least, any book on a topic in which you have a major interest. It may be genetics or pollution or something more specific like DNA or blood clotting. You may have a passion for learning how animals adapt to life in deserts, the territorial behaviour of certain fish or migration in birds. The nature of the topic hardly matters, provided you are interested. After all, reading is not intended as a form of punishment, but something to be enjoyed. The enforced reading of particular books is unlikely to engender a love of biology; it is far more likely to have you applying for a change of course. In any case you are unlikely to complete a book you don't enjoy and so will have gained little, if anything, from the exercise.

Don't feel that all reading has to be directly relevant to your syllabus. Any reading has some value. It will improve your English through the constant use of sentence construction and grammar. It will improve both your biological and non-biological vocabulary as you meet new words (provided you use an appropriate dictionary to discover their meaning). In this way reading will help you to become a more efficient communicator and so put across your ideas more coherently. As you meet different styles and approaches you will be able to adapt your own writing to include those you find effective. At the same time, you will doubtlessly learn new biological information as well as reinforcing what you already know. You may also be stimulated to do further reading, possibly on topics you had not previously considered. Make brief notes during your reading and add these to your other notes. Jot down page references as you go; you may need to refer back to these when writing some future essay.

It is important to distinguish between reading notes during revision and general reading. The former requires careful attention to each word because, if the notes have been taken properly, they will contain little or no superfluous information. In addition, as you are revising, it may be helpful to read parts a number of times to commit the information to memory. General reading must be much more rapid. Too many students read out loud. That is, they effectively say each word, if not audibly, at least to themselves. You should try to perfect a technique whereby the eyes skim rapidly across the lines, much faster than if the words were spoken. The brain is well capable of taking in the subject content at a speed faster than that necessary to speak the words. This speed reading is essential if enough books are to be completed to have a significant influence on your performance. Reading speed can normally be increased without any loss of comprehension. Try it and attempt to perfect it through practice. You may even consider taking one of the many speed-reading courses available.

Criticism and comment

None of us are so perfect that we are incapable of improvement. Constructive criticism and comment from others more experienced in a particular field is one sure way of upgrading performance. Books can provide information, guidance and help understanding but they cannot alone test how well the information is interpreted and communicated by an individual student. This is where your tutors come in.

Not everyone studies A-level biology full time in a school or college; an increasing number of candidates do so part time and without regular formal lessons. Most, however, still have access to a tutor as part of a distance-learning or supported self-study course. Whichever category you are in you should seek his/her advice and guidance throughout the course. Essays and other questions set during a course will normally be marked. When these are discussed it is vital to analyse your own shortcomings. Isolate where you have weaknesses. Is it that you don't read the question carefully? Having read the question accurately did you misinterpret what was required? Was the subject content inaccurate or inadequate? Was the detail lacking? Was there an absence of supporting evidence? Did you include too few examples? Did you fail to appreciate the underlying principles or did you get bogged down with unnecessary detail? Did you use the right references? Having determined where you went wrong, think of methods by which future work can avoid these problems. If necessary seek your tutor's advice.

Where individual comments are made on essays, take heed of them and determine not to make the same errors in future. A number of students ignore criticisms and simply repeat their failings time and time again. Apart from exasperating their tutor, this approach is hardly likely to effect an improvement. Learn to see all criticisms as positive; a means of isolating errors and providing an opportunity of putting them right. After all, if your work is beyond criticism you may as well take the A-level without further delay.

Ask for clarification of any comments if you are not sure to what they refer. Seek guidance on the best way to improve. Don't expect sudden or dramatic changes as this is unlikely. Aim to make slow, steady progress in partnership with your tutor.

2 HOW TO APPROACH EXAMINATIONS AND MODULAR TESTS

Whether you are taking a linear or modular course, your A-level grade will depend to a large extent on your performance in examinations. Before we look at the style of questions used in examinations and the techniques that should be employed to answer them successfully, let us begin by looking at the essential prerequisite for examination success – namely revision.

Revision

Revision is very much a personal affair and you should use the methods that suit you. Perhaps the best advice that one can give is to try as many variations as possible and then select those that bring the best results. Use tests and examinations throughout the course to try out different methods. It would be foolish to test a new technique during your final A-level revision; by that time you should have perfected your revision style.

At A-level, success is achieved by the gradual accumulation of knowledge and understanding throughout the course. The volume of knowledge is too great for it all to be absorbed during a few weeks' revision prior to the examinations. Try to read over notes daily, and if possible the whole week's work during the weekend. Prepare for interim tests and examinations thoroughly – only by so doing can you effectively test the efficiency of the revision methods you are using. Students who are disappointed by their final grade often admit to not having revised adequately for practice tests and examinations. How then could they have expected to know how much revision was needed for their actual examinations or modular tests? Always revise thoroughly for all examinations and analyse your results. If they were poor, change your revision methods.

Whichever method you use, here are 10 guidelines that can help you revise more effectively:

- Choose a place to work where distractions are unlikely. If possible sit at a desk or table, alone in a quiet room. Some students prefer to work with background noise such as music. This, however, may be distracting. For one thing there is the almost irresistible urge to sing along with the music – something that requires a degree of concentration. In addition the periodic need to change the radio station, cassette or compact disc will interrupt your concentration.
- Don't work for too long at a single session. The ability of the brain to concentrate, and so absorb information, diminishes rapidly after a while. The actual time varies with each individual but for most 1 hour is a reasonable maximum.
- Take breaks of 10–15 minutes between sessions. It helps if you leave the room you are using for study and do something very different – take the dog for a walk, watch television, exercise, play cards – anything provided it gives you a complete break from revision. Do things you really enjoy so that the breaks can be seen as a reward for your hard work.
- Be aware that, consciously or subconsciously, you will be seeking ways of avoiding doing revision. Fight the urge to give up. Let someone else answer

the door; don't leap up to answer the telephone. Make it clear to those around you that you have no wish to be disturbed.

- Be aware of 'displacement activities'. These are various activities that you carry out in order to bring relief from work. Revision is often boring and tedious and you will subconsciously be looking for a means of escape. The sudden craving for coffee or something to eat is no more than an excuse to stop work. You will hardly starve or die of thirst before your next break! There is no need to get up and look out of the window every time there is a noise, or to see whether or not it is raining. The cleaning of your shoes is not urgent and the dog can wait for a walk until later. Always be conscious of the dozens of trivial matters that suddenly assume great importance – and ignore them!

- Bring variety to your revision – vary the topics, subjects, times and place of revision and what you do in your breaks.

- Get feedback on the effectiveness of your revision by testing yourself or getting others to do so. Closing the book and immediately writing down what you can remember has little value as it tests only short-term memory. Success may depend on remembering information revised days or even weeks earlier. One useful technique is to write short questions as you revise and then try to answer them a day or so later. Even single words or dates can be jotted down, the significance of which you can later try to remember. Go back immediately and re-revise those questions you got wrong or could not answer.

- Practise problems or essays, preferably from past papers. Do them within the allocated time so you can practise working within limits. Study past papers to make yourself conversant with the styles of question. Be aware of any recent changes in the format or style of papers and questions. Predicting questions is a risky business and not worth the gamble.

- Use spare minutes for revision. It should be possible to read notes, or test yourself during the many spare moments in a day. The 10 minutes spent on a bus or train can be better occupied revising than reading the advertisements around you. The 5 minutes spent waiting for dinner or for someone to call can all be put to good effect. In themselves they may not be that much, but together they can make a significant contribution to the total revision. They could be the difference between a particular grade and the one above – in some cases the difference between a pass or failure.

- Organise revision by making a written timetable well in advance of examinations or modular tests. Be realistic. Do not make it so difficult that you fall behind schedule within the first week. Choose times to revise when you are less likely to be distracted. If you have an 'unfavourite' relative who visits on Wednesday evenings, put down at least 3 hours for this time – you have a better chance of achieving it than the evening of the local disco or your favourite television programme. Leave yourself at least one day a week with no revision, and leave one week in four completely free. This means that if an unexpected event arises, for example illness, you can use the 'free' days to compensate for lost time. If it does not prove necessary, then either use the time for additional revision or for rewarding a day off. The break may prove more valuable than revising as it will refresh you for future revision. Do not make a timetable for all your revision time. You will be extremely lucky if you do not have some situation that prevents you revising for at least some days in the weeks prior to the examinations.

Examination techniques

Having revised thoroughly and prepared yourself well for the examinations it would be a travesty to waste all this effort by making a hash of the actual papers. Good technique alone will not bring success but it will ensure your preparation brings its deserved reward. It is most important to use practice/trial/mock exams to perfect your methods – the final examination is no time to test their efficiency!

Students who perform well during their course, but fall-down when it comes to examinations, are often those who are over-dependent on books and/or tutors. Such over-reliance can mean that they do not acquire the skill of thinking for themselves and so when these crutches are removed during the examination, they collapse. Such failure is often blamed on 'not being good at exams' but is in fact the fault of bad preparation. Indeed much of the blame for poor results is wrongly excused as poor technique rather than the true culprit – inadequate preparation.

Perfecting a sound approach to examinations begins early in your course. It includes developing the ability to read critically, to think independently, and to answer questions, preferably from past papers and under time constraints. The latter will give you practice at interpreting questions and responding in concise, relevant terms. Most of all, you must learn from your mistakes to effect an improvement. Having achieved all this, along with careful revision, all that remains on the actual day is to apply the following common-sense points:

- Carry out all instructions to the letter. Do not assume them to be exactly the same as those you have seen on past papers.
- Act on any guidance given in the general instructions about the use of English, necessity for diagrams, need for orderly presentation, etc.
- Read all questions with great care. Do not be in a hurry to get started but rather be sure to understand what the question requires before answering.
- Where there is a choice of questions read *all* the questions first before making any selection. Read the paper a second time, making your choices, and finally read the selected questions a third time to ensure you have chosen ones you are competent to answer. Answer questions in any order but number them clearly.
- Often the total marks for the whole paper are stated. Divide this number into the time provided in order to find approximately how many minutes are available for each mark, e.g. 100 marks on a 3-hour paper gives:

$$\frac{180 \text{ minutes}}{100 \text{ marks}} = 1.8 \text{ minutes per mark}$$

Allowing time for reading this gives about 1.5 minutes per mark. You should therefore spend 15 minutes on a question worth 10 marks. Allocate your time for every question or part of a question in proportion to the marks available.

- Refer back to the question a number of times during the writing of an answer to ensure you have not strayed from the point. Re-read the question once you have completed your answer in case you have omitted any part.
- Try to isolate the key-word or words in a question and answer precisely in accordance with them (see the list on p. 15).
- Try to be completely relevant, clear and concise in your answers. Do not ramble, repeat yourself or try to disguise inadequate knowledge by waffling or straying from the point.
- Check during the last quarter of a paper that you have followed all instructions carefully and have answered (or are about to) the requisite number of questions. Do not leave this until the last 5 minutes – it will be too late to put right should you have made an error.

Question types

The style of examination questions set in A-level biology by the examination boards has become increasingly standardised over recent years. While some open-ended/open-response/open-prose/essay type questions persist and more rarely multiple-choice questions, the majority are now structured questions that are divided into separate small parts and are answered in the space provided on the question sheet.

Structured (short-answer) questions

There is great variation in this type of question. In its simplest form only a single word answer is required e.g. 'Name the enzyme that hydrolyses starch to maltose'. Some demand a short sentence e.g. 'What is the function of follicle stimulating hormone?' while others require a longer response e.g. 'Describe how you would carry out Gram's staining technique on a sample of bacteria'. These types of questions may require you to demonstrate any of the following skills:

- Show knowledge and understanding of biological terms, concepts, principles and relationships.
- Construct hypotheses.
- Design experiments.
- Interpret the results of experiments.
- Draw conclusions and make inferences.
- Assess and evaluate numerical and non-numerical information.
- Explain observations and solve problems.
- Present data in its many varied forms.
- Comprehend, interpret and translate data.
- Criticise material and exercise biological judgement.
- Construct or label diagrams of biological importance.
- Interpret or comment on photographs.
- Collect, collate and summarise biological information in an appropriate form.
- Appreciate the social, environmental, economic and technological applications of biology.

In structured questions it is content rather than style that is being tested and so answers should be clear and concise and to the point; note-style responses are acceptable. The marks allocated and the space provided for the answer usually give an indication of the amount of detail required.

Essay (free-response) questions

Most examination boards set at least one question that requires you to produce a longer answer often in the form of a short essay. Being open-ended such questions do not limit you to one particular response but rather give you the scope to demonstrate the depth and breadth of your biological knowledge. It is often for this reason that students dislike them – they are uncertain of what exactly the question requires and/or lack the range and detail of knowledge needed to answer them effectively. Equally there are some who fare badly on essay questions for the opposite reason – they digress widely from the question, using it as an opportunity to relate the last biological article they read or indulge their opinions with little regard to their relevance. The skill lies in achieving a compromise between these two extremes.

Essay questions may be structured to some degree. In a highly structured essay the question comprises a number of different parts that often guide you step-by-step through the question, making clear at each stage exactly what is required. To take a typical example:

(a)   Explain what is meant by the terms:
  (i) enzyme.
  (ii) coenzyme   (*4 marks*)
(b)   With reference to the lock and key theory, and active sites explain how an enzyme works.   (*8 marks*)
(c)   What are the factors that influence the rate of enzyme activity? Briefly point out why the factors you mention alter the rate.   (*8 marks*)

The figures in brackets represent the marks allocated to each section – a common feature of the structured essay. These marks provide clear guidance on how long should be spent on each part. In this example it is relatively clear what the examiner is looking for at each stage. The answer to this question might not be very different from one entitled 'Write an essay on enzymes' but we suspect that you would find the latter more problematic because you cannot be sure what the examiner wants and therefore what to include and what to leave out. The structured essay overcomes these problems to some degree, but you should never neglect careful planning. Under each subsection of the question it is necessary to jot down the essential points to be made before starting your answer. Only in this way can your response be logically argued with well-marshalled ideas and relevant supporting evidence. You should answer each part separately – never attempt to merge them into a general essay. Take care not to use information more than once as you cannot be given credit twice for the same explanation. In the question cited it would be feasible to include the lock and key theory in all three parts. This would be a waste of examination time. It is almost certainly to avoid this problem that the examiners have guided you to include this information in part (b).

An alternative type of essay is the unstructured one. This may be as open ended as 'Write an essay on enzymes/carbohydrates/animal reproduction/photosynthesis/hormones', etc. In practice they are often a little more explicit:

- Describe the properties of water and show why it is vital to living organisms.
- Describe how animals depend for their survival on the activities of plants.
- Argue a case for and against the use of pesticides and fertilisers.

In this style of essay, planning is more crucial. The number of points that could be made is vast and the skill is limiting them to the most important, i.e. those most likely to be on the examiners' mark scheme. In the 30–40 minutes typically allowed for an essay question, only perhaps 20 or 30 individual facts can be included in sufficient detail to warrant marks. You must ensure that these points cover the full range of the topic being examined. Take, for example, the following essay: 'Write an essay on movement in organisms'.

There is a danger here that all points made will be biased towards the movement of whole organisms (locomotion) and animals. Good planning (and adequate knowledge) can avoid this. Movement in biology includes the movement of material within an organism and within and between cells. All living things use movement. Your essay should therefore encompass all types of movement and a wide range of organisms – plant, animal and protoctista. Avoid any bias towards animals, especially mammals.

The main areas on your plan should be:

Types of movement	Example
Subatomic movement	Electron movement in photosynthesis
Atomic/ionic/molecular	Diffusion, osmosis, active transport into and out of cells; transpiration, translocation
Cellular	Amoeboid, ciliate, flagellate locomotion; movement of macrophages
Tissue/organ	Heart pumping, circulation of blood
Organism	Locomotion, swimming, flying, burrowing, etc.
Population	Migrations

Include each of the six areas listed but try to link them in a coherent manner. Some examination boards give marks for the manner in which the essay is written, its fluency, clarity and logical arguments.

The wording of essay questions is all important. There are subtle differences between terms such as 'compare', 'describe', 'discuss' and 'distinguish'. Unless you appreciate this you are likely to needlessly throw away marks. The following list is a guide to the appropriate meaning of a number of commonly occurring question terms.

Describe	Give an account of the main points, with reference to (visual) observations if possible.
Explain/Account for	Show how and why; give reasons for – with reference to theory, if possible.
Compare	Point out differences and similarities.
Distinguish/Contrast	Make distinctions between, point out differences.
Discuss	Debate, giving the various viewpoints and arguments.
Criticise	Point out faults and shortcomings.
Survey	Give a comprehensive and extensive review.
Comment on	Make remarks and observations on.
Illustrated	Use figures, drawings, diagrams.
Annotate	Add notes of explanation.
Calculate	A numerical answer is required and working should be shown.
Briefly/Concisely	Give a short statement of only the main points.
Outline	Give the essential points, briefly.
List	Catalogue, often as a sequence of words one beneath the other.
Significance	Importance of.
State	Set down concisely with little or no supporting evidence.
Define	Give only a formal statement.
Suggest	Put forward ideas, thoughts, hypotheses.
Devise	Construct, compose, make up.
Estimate	Give a reasonable approximation.

Multiple-choice questions

Now much less frequently used in A-level biology examinations, multiple-choice questions vary in style but generally comprise a statement or question followed by five alternative answers. You are then required to select the most appropriate response from these alternatives. For example:

In the electron (hydrogen) carrier system of aerobic respiration, which of the following is the last stage?

A   formation of ATP
B   reduction of oxygen
C   production of carbon dioxide
D   reduction of cytochrome
E   production of H^+ (Answer = B)

In approaching multiple-choice questions you should read through the whole question and *all* the alternatives before making your choice because often more than one will be correct to some degree. It is the best, or most appropriate answer that is required. On reading again reject those responses you feel are clearly incorrect. Always reject on a sound biological basis and never because it 'doesn't sound right' or because 'it can't be B for the fifth time on the trot'. Should you still be left with more than one answer try to find a good reason why one response is better than another. If you simply cannot decide for valid reasons then, as a last resort, guess. Unless the rubric states otherwise there is no penalty for a wrong answer and so a guess is better than giving no response.

Modular tests

Preparation for modular tests and the examination techniques you need to apply to them are largely the same as for other written examinations. However, the following points should be remembered when taking modular tests.

- The modular examinations, even where taken after only one term of study, are marked to the same standard as terminal examinations. No concession is made for your relative inexperience at A-level study.
- The modular examination usually carries a narrower range of material than other examinations. Do not be lulled into thinking that preparation can be less thorough and/or less urgent.
- The time interval between the practice (mock) test and the actual examination is likely to be short, leaving little time to compensate for deficiencies in knowledge and/or technique.
- Terminal examinations (which are those taken after 14 February in the final year) must contribute at least 30% of the final mark/grade. These later modules often incorporate skills and understanding that have been acquired in previous modules. Do not assume all previous knowledge can be forgotten.
- Modular tests are typically $1-1\frac{1}{2}$ hours in duration. Their relative shortness makes the management of your time especially important as there is little opportunity to compensate for lost time. Answers need to be concise and to the point.
- There is little respite from examinations, no sooner is one complete than the next appears on the horizon. Take care not to become fatigued but to adequately build yourself up mentally for the next module.

Final preparation

Provided you have prepared an adequate revision timetable, begun the process early and followed it through faithfully, there should be little left to do on the evening prior to your examination. If you have not revised adequately it is a mistake to imagine that a few hours of cramming can compensate for your earlier omissions.

The best advice we can give for the evening prior to an examination is to try to relax and have a good night's rest. You may find it difficult to follow this advice as it demands great confidence that your revision has been complete. If you simply cannot bring yourself to do no work, we would suggest a quick skim through your notes or textbook, perhaps reading headings and subheadings, to generally absorb ideas and principles. Equally, there may be a few equations, definitions or mnemonics that you might wish to reinforce in your memory. Avoid, however, detailed revision of topics as it is almost certainly too late for this to be of benefit and there is the very real risk of inducing panic as you struggle to come to grips with a difficult concept. This will only create confusion and undermine your confidence, making matters worse than if no work had been done at all.

Our advice is therefore to keep any revision low key, to prepare the necessary examination materials (pens, pencils, calculator, etc.) for the following day, relax, set your alarm and get a good night's sleep.

PART 2

TOPIC OUTLINES
AND QUESTIONS

3 LEVELS OF ORGANISATION

Atomic and molecular organisation

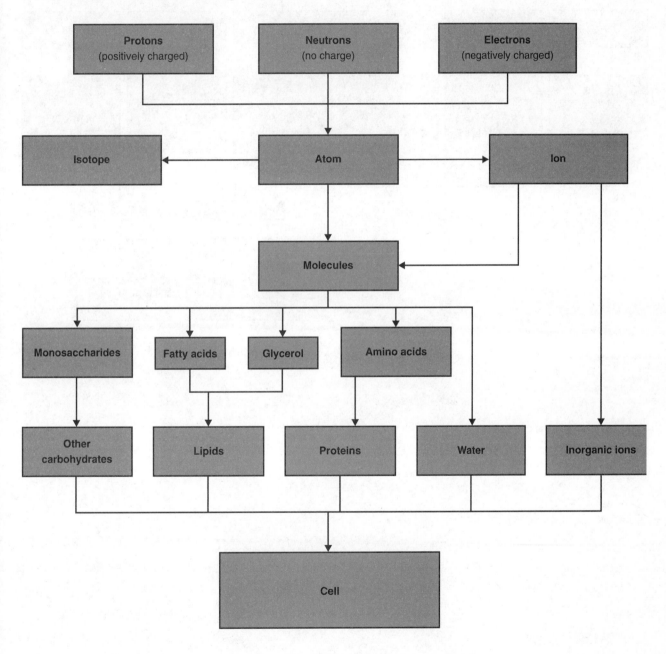

Movement in and out of cells

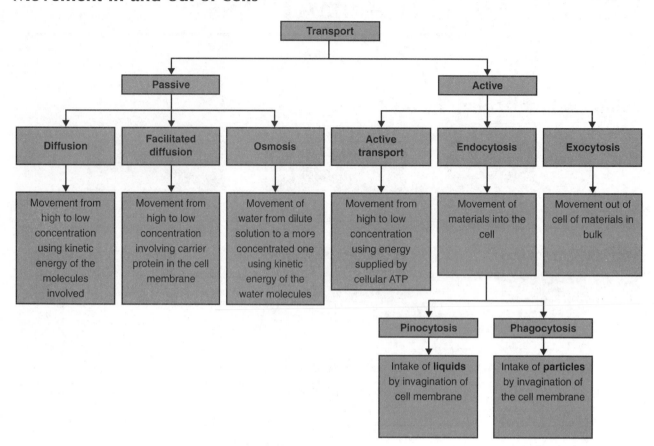

Cellular organisation

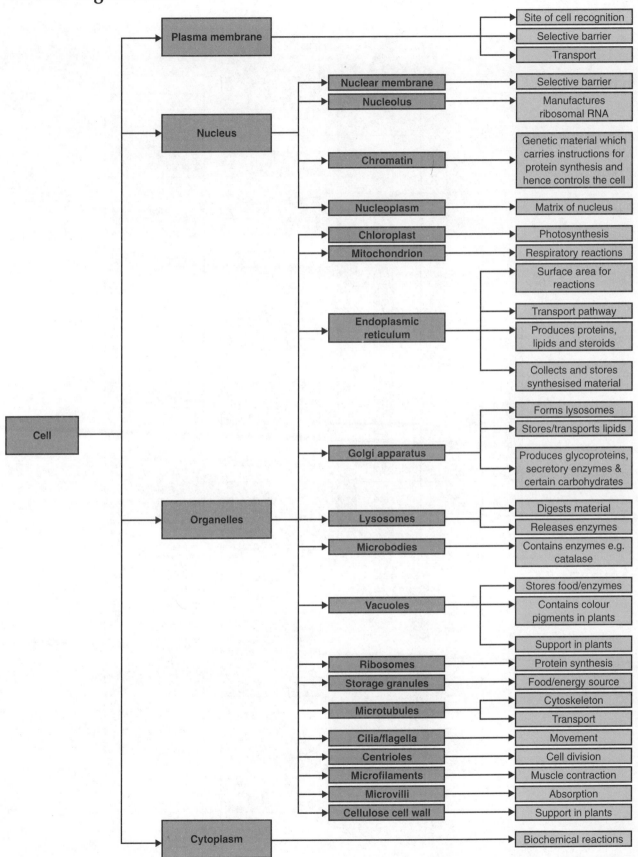

Classification of organisms

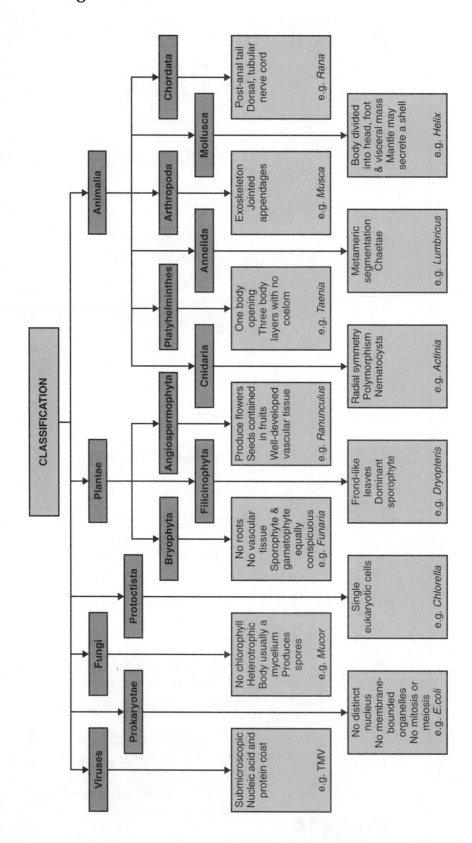

Testing and applying knowledge on levels of organisation

1. (a) (i) Which chemical element contains one proton and one electron?

(ii) Give the name of the chemical formed if an atomic particle with no overall charge is added to this element.

(iii) What is the general name for this new element?

(iv) By what percentage is its atomic mass altered by the addition of this new particle?

(v) How is the atomic number affected by the addition of this new particle?

(b) (i) What is formed if a negatively charged particle is removed from a hydrogen atom?

(ii) How is the atomic mass changed by the addition of this negatively charged particle?

(iii) What name is given to the process by which this negatively charged particle is removed from the element?

2. Study the molecules shown in the figure below. (NB: In some of the molecules, the atoms have been omitted for simplicity.)

A

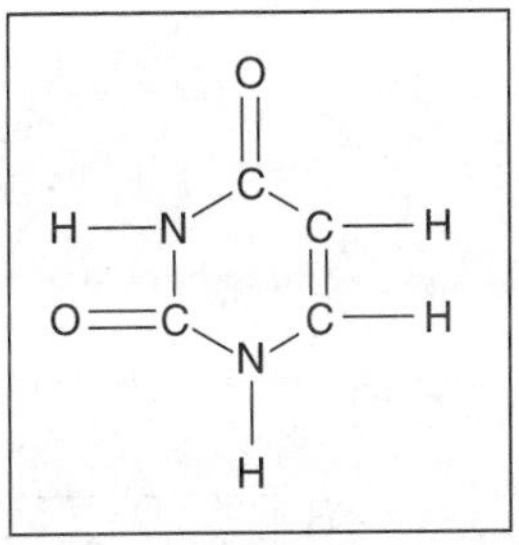

B

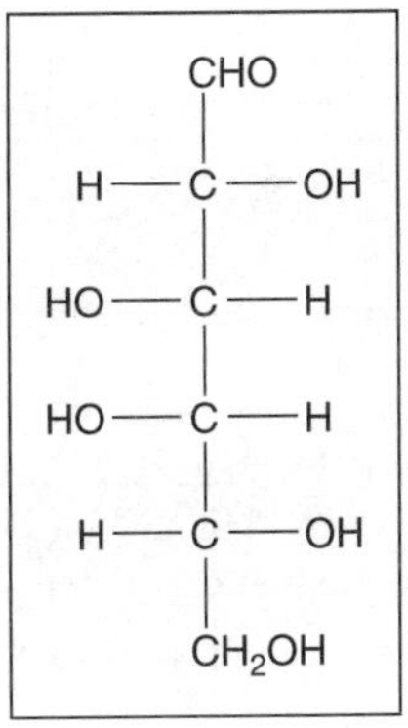

C

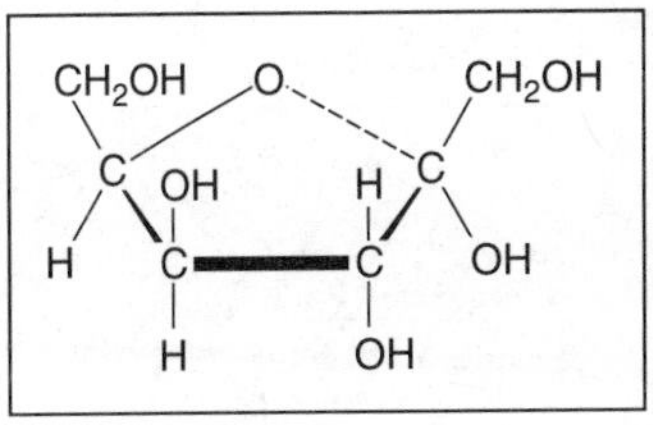

D

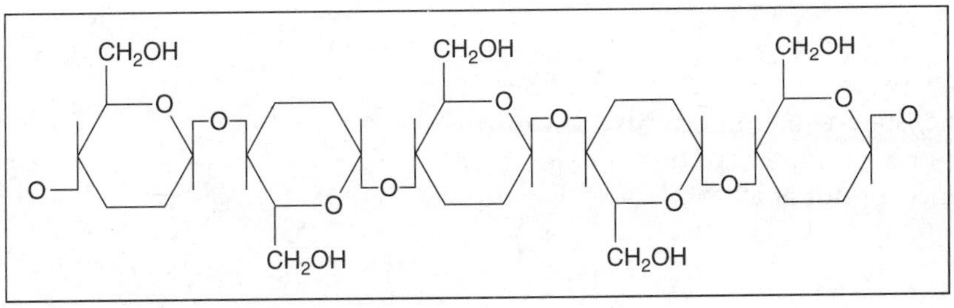

E

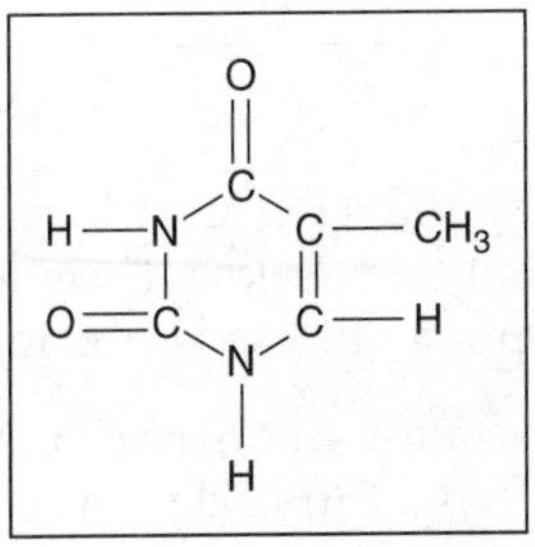

F

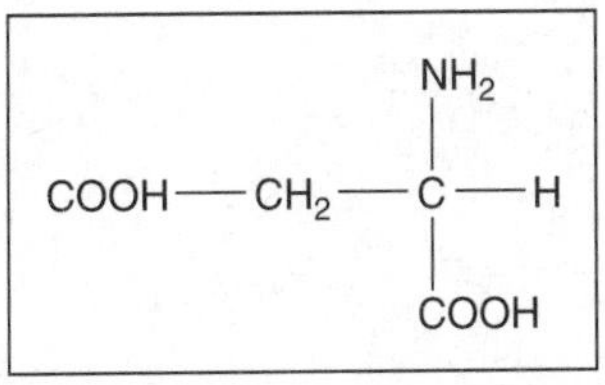

G

$C_{17}H_{35}COOH$

H

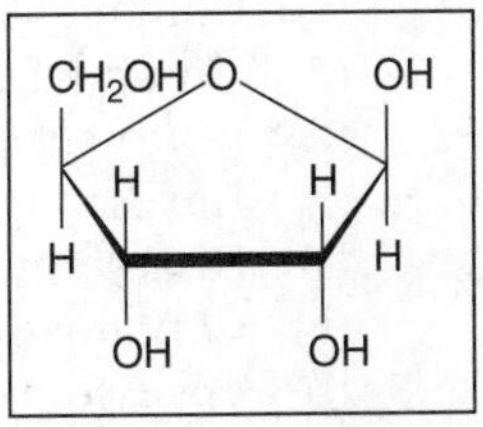

I

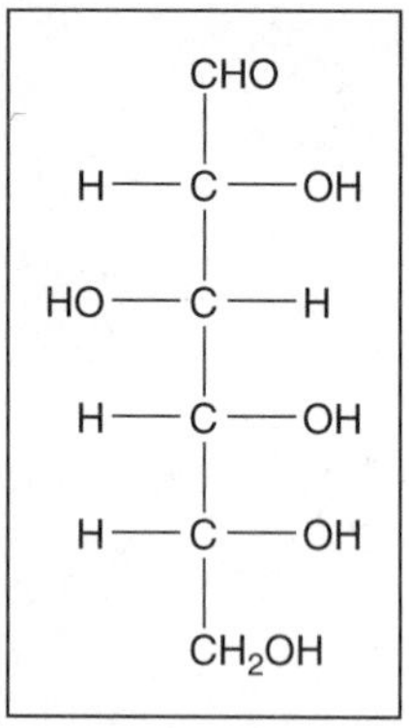

$$CHO$$
$$H-C-OH$$
$$HO-C-H$$
$$H-C-OH$$
$$H-C-OH$$
$$CH_2OH$$

J

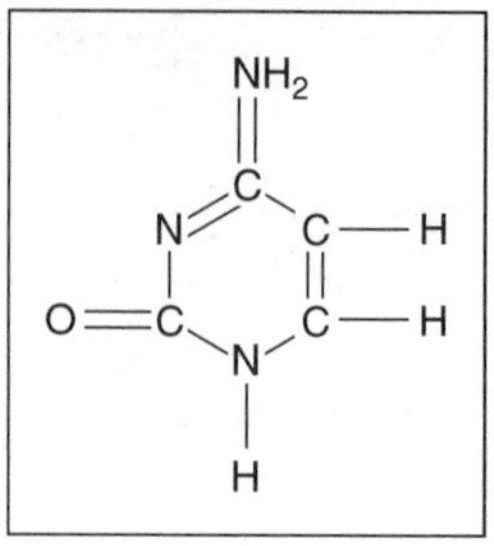

NH_2 ... N, $C-H$, $O=C$, $C-H$, N, H

K

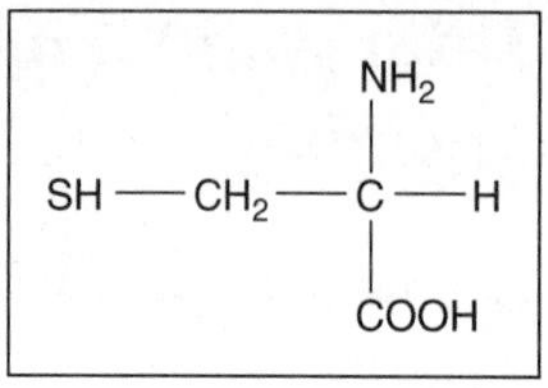

$$SH-CH_2-C-H$$ with NH_2 above and $COOH$ below

L

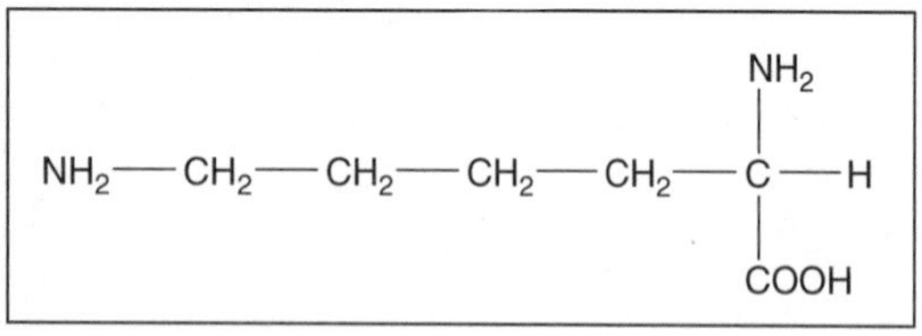

$$NH_2-CH_2-CH_2-CH_2-CH_2-C-H$$ with NH_2 above and $COOH$ below

M

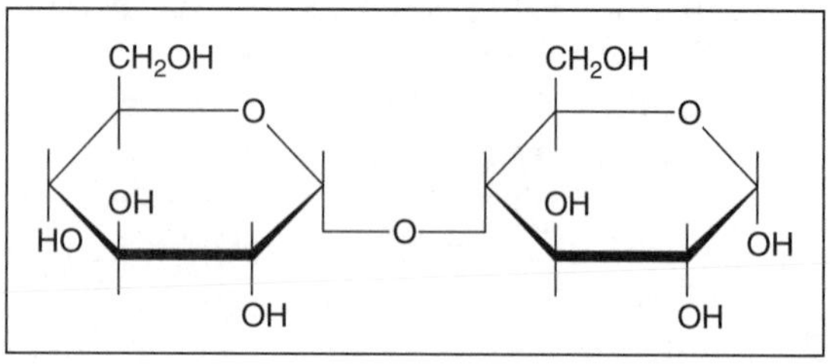

Two ring sugar structures with CH_2OH, OH, HO, linked by O

N

$C_{17}H_{31}COOH$

O

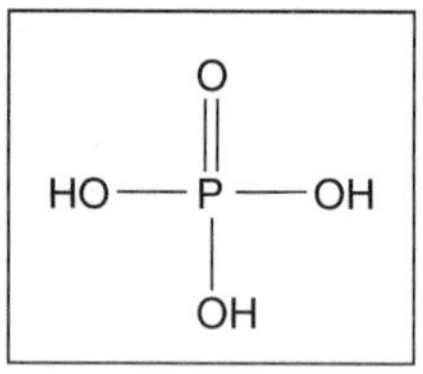

$$HO-P-OH$$ with O above and OH below

P

Purine-type ring structure with O, $H-N$, C, C, N, $C-H$, $H_2N=C$, N, C, N, H

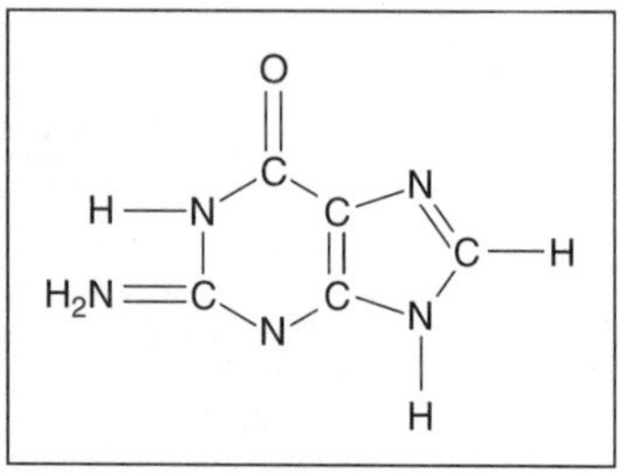

Q

$$H-C-H$$ with NH_2 above and $COOH$ below

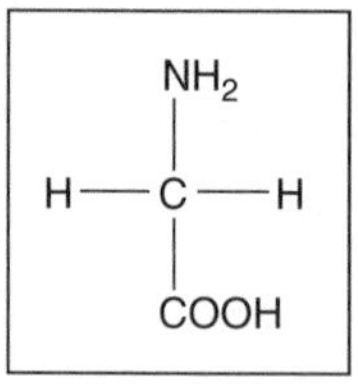

R

$C_{17}H_{33}COOH$

Using the letter next to each molecule, state which one(s) fits each of the descriptions below. There may be just one, or more than one, answer. Each letter may be used once, more than once, or not at all.

- (a) Carbohydrate molecule(s)
- (b) Fatty acid molecule(s)
- (c) Amino acid molecule(s)
- (d) Contain hydroxyl group(s)
- (e) Contain amino group(s)
- (f) Contain aldehyde group(s)
- (g) Unsaturated molecule(s)
- (h) Pentose sugar(s)
- (i) Hexose sugar(s)
- (j) Disaccharide(s)
- (k) Contain glycosidic bond(s)
- (l) The two pairs that are isomers of one another

3.   (a) What name is given to the small part of an enzyme molecule that comes in contact with its substrate?

(b) The number of substrate molecules upon which an enzyme can act in a given time is called what?

(c) Give an example of a non-reversible inhibitor.

(d) Name the coenzyme associated with dehydrogenase enzymes in respiration.

(e) What term is used to describe any organic cofactor that is bound to an enzyme?

4.   A – Cell membrane   J – Chloroplast
B – Nucleus   K – Microbody (peroxisome)
C – Nucleolus   L – Vacuole
D – Cytoplasmic matrix   M – Microtubule
E – Mitochondrion   N – Centriole
F – Endoplasmic reticulum   O – Flagellum
G – Lysosome   P – Cilium
H – Ribosome   Q – Microfilament
I – Golgi apparatus

Match one of the above cell organelles with each of the statements below. Each organelle may be used once, more than once, or not at all.

(a) It has two forms – rough and smooth.
(b) It is usually made up of the protein actin.
(c) It is larger in eukaryotic cells at 20 nm than it is in prokaryotic cells.
(d) It has cisternae and fenestrations.
(e) In plant cells it is known as a dictyosome.
(f) This organelle may be up to 100 μm long.
(g) It carries out autophagy.
(h) It is made up of alpha- and beta-tubulin.
(i) A pair may be poles apart.
(j) The spindle found during cell division is made of these.
(k) It manufactures ribosomal RNA.
(l) It isolates the enzyme that breaks down hydrogen peroxide.
(m) It contains grana.
(n) In plants it is surrounded by a tonoplast.
(o) It produces glycoproteins such as mucin.

5.   A – Diffusion
B – Osmosis
C – Facilitated diffusion
D – Active transport
E – Phagocytosis
F – Pinocytosis

The answers to the following questions are found in the above list of methods of transport in and out of a cell.

(a) Both these forms of transport use carrier proteins.
(b) It only occurs across a differentially permeable membrane.
(c) Which **two** processes are examples of endocytosis?
(d) White blood cells ingest harmful bacteria by this method.
(e) Cyanide would halt **three** of the processes – which?

Answers to testing and applying knowledge on levels of organisation

1. (a) (i)   Hydrogen
        (ii) Deuterium (the particle with no overall charge is a neutron).
        (iii) An isotope
        (iv) 100% (i.e. it is doubled, as neutrons have a similar mass to protons).
        (v)   It is unaltered (the atomic number is the number of protons only, and this remains as one).

    (b) (i)   A hydrogen ion (the negatively charged particle is an electron).
        (ii) It is not changed (the electron has a negligible atomic mass).
        (iii) Oxidation

2. (a) B, C, D, H, I, M
    (b) G, N, R
    (c) F, K, L, Q
    (d) B, C, D, H, I, M, O
    (e) F, J, K, L, P, Q
    (f) B, I
    (g) A, E, J, N, O, P, R
    (h) H
    (i) B, C, I
    (j) M
    (k) M, D
    (l) B and I, C and H

3. (a) Active site
    (b) Turnover value
    (c) Heavy metal ions such as mercury (Hg^{2+}) and silver (Ag^+)
    (d) Nicotinamide adenine dinucleotide (NAD) / Flavine adenine dinucleotide (FAD)
    (e) Prosthetic group

4. (a) F – Endoplasmic reticulum
    (b) Q – Microfilament
    (c) H – Ribosome
    (d) F – Endoplasmic reticulum
    (e) I – Golgi apparatus
    (f) O – Flagellum
    (g) G – Lysosome
    (h) M – Microtubule
    (i) N – Centriole
    (j) M – Microtubule
    (k) C – Nucleolus
    (l) K – Microbody
    (m) J – Chloroplast
    (n) L – Vacuole
    (o) I – Golgi apparatus

5. (a) C (Facilitated diffusion) and D (Active transport)
    (b) B (Osmosis)
    (c) E (Phagocytosis) and F (Pinocytosis)
    (d) E (Phagocytosis)
    (e) D (Active transport), E (Phagocytosis) and F (Pincytosis)

Sample question on levels of organisation

(a)   What is an enzyme?   (*3 marks*)

(b)   At a constant pH and enzyme concentration, the effect on the rate of reaction was measured at different concentrations of substrate. The following graph was obtained:

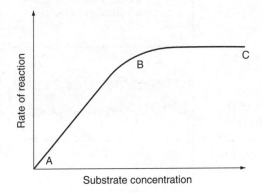

(i)   Explain what is happening at points A, B and C.   (*6 marks*)
(ii)   The original experiment was carried out at 30°C. Sketch on the graph the curve that would have been plotted had the experiment been carried out at 20°C.   (*3 marks*)

(c)   In a further experiment, substances 1 and 2 were added to an enzyme working on its substrate. Additional substrate was also added later, and the rate of enzyme reaction was measured. The following graphs were obtained:

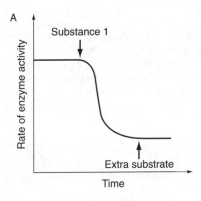

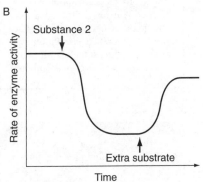

Explain what is happening in
    (i)   graph A   (*3 marks*)
    (ii) graph B   (*3 marks*)
                            (*Total 18 marks*)

Guided response to sample question on levels of organisation

(a)   It is reasonable to assume that you need to make separate points to obtain all three marks. A typical response should refer to both an enzyme's chemical structure and its mode of action as shown in the answer below:

√ A complex three-dimensional globular protein with catalytic properties (i.e. it alters the rate of chemical reaction without itself undergoing permanent change).
√ It functions in small quantities by a specific part of the enzyme, the active site, coming into contact with its substrate.

(b)   (i) With six marks (and hence 6 minutes) available for this part of the question you need to make two distinct statements on each of the three points. For example you should state the relationship between the rate of enzyme reaction and the substrate concentration for one mark and follow it with the reasons for this relationship for the second mark. The answer might appear something like:

Point A –
√ As the amount of substrate increases so does the rate of reaction.
√ This means that not all the enzyme's active sites are occupied by substrate molecules and so when more substrate molecules are added there are enzyme molecules available to convert them to more product (i.e. the substrate limits the rate of reaction).

Point B –
√ While the addition of further substrate still increases the rate of reaction it does so at a diminishing rate.
√ This is because most enzymes have their active sites occupied by substrate molecules at any one time, and it therefore takes longer for the free substrate molecules to come into contact with the diminishing number of vacant active sites.

Point C –
√ Despite further increases in the amount of substrate, the rate of reaction remains constant.
√ because all the enzyme molecule's active sites are occupied with substrate molecules at any point in time, i.e. the turnover rate of the enzyme is at a maximum.

(ii)   To obtain full marks, your sketch will need to be the correct shape and be positioned absolutely accurately. The shape is roughly the same as the original line but as the temperature is lower it takes longer for the enzyme and substrate molecules to come into contact because they are moving more slowly. The initial gradient is therefore reduced, i.e. point 'A' is displaced to the right. The temperature difference of 10°C is significant as such a reduction **halves** the rate of reaction. Point 'C' is therefore at half its original height. The sketch graph should appear as shown over:

TUTORIAL TIP

Always read through the **whole** question before attempting any part of it. This will help you to make your responses in the most relevant part of the question rather than repeating yourself.

TUTORIAL TIP

Calculate the time available for each question and then apportion the time to each part according to the marks allocated, e.g. If 20 minutes were available for this 18-mark question, each mark warrants approximately 1 minute of your time, allowing time for reading.

TUTORIAL TIP

Deal with points A, B and C entirely independently as though they were separate questions. This will avoid the confusion that can arise if you try to provide a single mixed answer.

TUTORIAL TIP

The word 'explain' requires you to **give reasons** for the shape of the graph at each point and not just to describe the relationship between the rate of reaction and the substrate concentration.

TUTORIAL TIP

Where precise values are given (e.g. 20°C and 30°C) always consider the possibility that these values are significant as in this case.

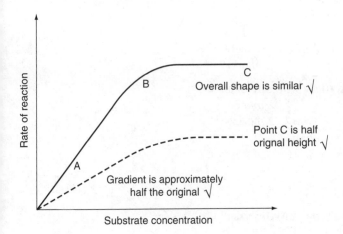

(c)   Substances 1 and 2 both reduce the rate of reaction and are hence inhibitors. However, while the effect of substance 1 is not affected by an increase in the quantity of substrate, the inhibitory effect of substance 2 is reversed by such an addition. Substance 1 therefore causes **irreversible** inhibition while substance 2 causes **reversible** inhibition. The word 'explain' is significant and you must give **reasons** for this difference along the lines of the answer below:

(i)   √ Substance 1 is similar in molecular shape to the substrate and therefore:
√ fits into the enzyme's active site permanently (or may permanently damage the active site),
√ thus preventing substrate molecules from fitting the active site.

(ii) √ Substance 2 will fit into the enzyme's active site but this is a loose fit and it can easily be displaced.
√ As more substrate is added there is a greater chance of a substrate molecule finding an active site.
√ The amount of inhibition is reduced because there is less chance of an inhibitor molecule entering an active site than a substrate molecule.

Practice questions on levels of organisation

Q. 1
Distinguish between the following:
(a)   monosaccharides and polysaccharides;   (*2 marks*)
(b)   starch and cellulose;   (*2 marks*)
(c)   saturated and unsaturated fats;   (*2 marks*)
(d)   globular and fibrous proteins.   (*2 marks*)
                                                          (*Total 8 marks*)

Q. 2
(a)   Give the basic structure of an amino acid.   (*2 marks*)

(b)   Name the two groups that occur in all amino acids.   (*2 marks*)

(c)   (i) Show by means of a diagram how two amino acids combine to form a dipeptide.   (*3 marks*)

(ii) What is the name given to the bond formed between two amino acids? *(1 mark)*

(iii) What **type** of reaction would break this chemical bond between the two acids? *(1 mark)*

(d) State **two** differences between the secondary and tertiary structure of a protein molecule. *(2 marks)*

(Total 11 marks)

Q. 3

Enzyme X is the product of thermophilic (heat-loving) bacteria. It hydrolyses many proteins including haemoglobin and egg albumin.

Enzyme Y is found in the stomach of young mammals where it acts on a single soluble protein found in milk, causing it to coagulate.

(a) (i) From the descriptions, comment on the differences in the specificity of the two enzymes. *(2 marks)*

(ii) Enzymes X and Y are each used for different commercial purposes. Suggest what this might be in each case. *(2 marks)*

(iii) Explain the purpose of enzyme Y in the mammalian stomach. *(3 marks)*

(iv) Where might thermophilic bacteria occur naturally? *(1 mark)*

(b) An experiment was carried out with enzyme X in which the time taken for it to fully hydrolyse 5 grams of its protein substrate was measured at different temperatures. The following data were obtained:

Temp (°C)	Time (min) for hydrolysis of protein	Rate of reaction (1/time)
15	5.8	
25	3.4	
35	1.7	
45	0.7	
55	0.6	
65	0.9	
75	7.1	

(i) Calculate the values for 1/time and add them to the right hand column. *(1 mark)*

(ii) Plot a graph that illustrates the effect of temperature on the rate of reaction of enzyme X. *(4 marks)*

(iii) What is the optimum temperature for the action of enzyme X? *(1 mark)*

(iv) How would you determine this optimum temperature more precisely? *(3 marks)*

(Total 17 marks)

TUTORIAL TIP

When plotting graphs, choose the axes and scale carefully so that they cover as much as possible of the available paper, and allow you to plot the points easily. Label the axes clearly, state the units and put a title on the graph.

Q. 4

Below is a diagram of a generalised animal cell. Study it carefully and answer the questions that follow.

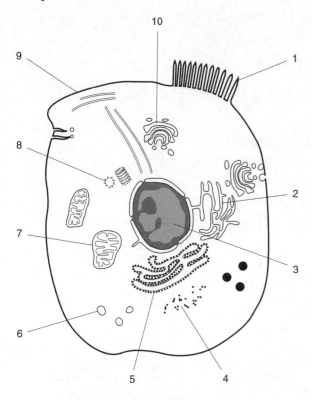

(a) Label the parts indicated by the numbers 1–10. (*10 marks*)

(b) Name **two** features of the cell that distinguish it from a prokaryotic cell. (*2 marks*)

(c) State **three** functions of the structure labelled 10. (*3 marks*)

(d) Give the label number of the organelle that most closely fits the following descriptions. Give **one** number for each description. Each number may be used once, more then once or not at all.
    (i) Carries out autophagy.
    (ii) Made up of a series of flattened sacs, but lacks ribosomes.
    (iii) Involved in protein synthesis.
    (iv) Possesses stalked granules.
    (v) Contains an enzyme that is inhibited by cyanide.
    (*5 marks*)

(e) Give the numbers of the **two** organelles that you would expect to be numerous and well-developed in a cell carrying out absorption. (*2 marks*)

(f) If organelle 7 were 32 mm in length on the diagram, and the diagram was magnified 16 000 times. State the actual size of the organelle in μm. Show your working. (*3 marks*)
(*Total 25 marks*)

Q. 5

(a)   Why are organisms classified?   *(2 marks)*

(b)   Place the following list of taxonomic groups in ascending order beginning with the smallest unit of classification and finishing with the largest:

class; phylum; species; order; family; genus   *(1 mark)*

(c)   Explain why a virus can be considered as both living and non-living.
                                                               (2 marks)
                                                          (Total 5 marks)

Q. 6

Read the following passage carefully and then using the information it
contains and your own biological knowledge answer the questions below.

Yellow fields of oilseed rape are nowadays a common (some would say
too common) sight, and beautiful blue fields of linseed add another
contrasting colour to the traditional green of the British country-
side. Both these crops are grown for oil.

After cereals, oil crops are the second most important provider of   5
food energy for human societies. Oil crops are also a potential
source of a large variety of non-edible products. These range from
high-value pharmaceuticals and cosmetics to basic industrial raw
materials and even fuels. Because there are still relatively large
quantities of cheap, fossil-derived mineral oil (e.g. from the   10
North Sea), less than 20% of the world's output of vegetable oil is
used for non-edible purposes. It is now recognised that mineral
oils are a non-renewable resource and, at current rates of consump-
tion, latest estimates are that the known resources will start to run
out within the next 40-50 years. This is because mineral oils are   15
ultimately derived from the remains of plants that grew, died and
became fossilised over a period of hundreds of thousands of years
during the Carboniferous period, some 300 million years ago. Once
these oil stocks are used up they cannot be replaced.

This means that there will be an ever increasing demand for vege-   20
table oils in order to satisfy markets currently supplied by mineral
oils. In order to supply the correct type of vegetable oil required
for a particular end use, it will be necessary for research scientists and plant breeders to cooperate in the production of new
varieties of oil crops.   25

In all plants, oils are made initially from carbohydrates, such as
sucrose, which are produced during photosynthesis. The sucrose is
broken down during glycolysis and acetyl CoA is produced. This
acetyl CoA is then converted into fatty acids.

It is the varied chemical composition of the fatty acid components   30
of triglycerides which gives vegetable oils their specific properties. For example, very long-chain fatty acids, containing 22 or
more carbon atoms, will give rise to relatively heavy oils, useful
for the production of lubricants and cosmetics. On the other hand,
relatively short-chain fatty acids, containing 10 to 14 carbon   35
atoms, will produce oils that are useful sources of detergents for
washing and cleaning. Fatty acids containing two or more double
bonds are readily oxidised to form polymerised solid products.
This makes them ideal coating agents in paints, varnishes and
putties.   40

Unlike animals, plants are able to produce a huge range of fatty
acids by means of specific modification enzymes such as hydroxy-
lases, epoxidases, elongases, desaturases, etc. Unfortunately not

all plant species contain these fatty acid modification enzymes. For
example, the most important European oilseed crops are sunflower and 45
rapeseed. Both of these crops produce seed oils containing over 90%
18-carbon fatty acids which make for useful edible oils. However, if
we wish to modify these crops to produce different oils with different properties, it will be necessary to insert the genes for the
necessary modifying enzymes. These genes can only be obtained from 50
the plants that normally produce the enzymes. This is where genetic
engineering comes in.

The most efficient way to transfer genes into plants is to use a
bacterium, such as *Agrobacterium tumefaciens*, as a vector of the
introduced DNA. The fragment of DNA transferred by the bacterium 55
must contain the genes of interest plus an extra gene encoding for
an antibiotic resistance gene. This second gene is included so
that scientists can tell which of the host cells has been 'transformed' from those that have not taken up the new DNA fragments. If
all of the host cells of the plant are then treated with antibiotics, 60
only the transformed cells containing the gene of interest and the
antibiotic resistance gene will survive. Antibiotics will kill
all untransformed plant cells by disrupting their cellular metabolism. Transformed cells containing the antibiotic resistance
gene are able to break down the toxic antibiotic and will therefore 65
survive and continue to divide. These surviving transformed plant
cells can then be grown in tissue culture and will eventually regen-
erate complete plants.

It is important that the introduced gene should be expressed only
in the relevant tissue (i.e. the seed) and at the correct time (i.e. 70
during seed development). Gene expression should also be at a high
enough level to produce sufficient quantities of the enzyme to
produce enough of the oil.

It is likely that the coming years will see the manipulation of
more and more major oil crops for the production of useful, non- 75
edible vegetable oils. In the short-term, this will be an attractive
way to use surplus agricultural land within Europe.

From 'Genetically Engineered Plant Oils' an article by
Denis Murphy in the *Biological Sciences Review*, Vol. 6, No. 5.

(a)   Explain what is meant by the following terms in the passage:
       (i)   'non-renewable' (line 13)   (*1 mark*)
       (ii) 'triglycerides' (line 31)   (*1 mark*)
       (iii) 'vector' (line 54)   (*1 mark*)

(b)   (i) Give **two** current uses of 'fossil-derived mineral oil' (line 10).
                                                              (*2 marks*)

       (ii) State **three** possible advantages of mankind using oil derived from
       crops rather than fossil-derived mineral oil.   (*3 marks*)

(c)   Summarise the main stages by which 'sucrose is broken down during
       glycolysis and acetyl CoA is produced' (lines 27 and 28).   (*5 marks*)

(d)   Suggest explanations for the following statements:
       (i)   'It is important that the introduced gene should be expressed only
       in the relevant tissue (i.e. the seed)' (lines 69–70).   (*1 mark*)
       (ii) 'Gene expression should also be at a level to produce sufficient
       quantities of the enzyme to produce enough of the oil' (lines 71–73).
                                                              (*1 mark*)
                                                         (*Total 15 marks*)

Answers to practice questions on levels of organisation

1. Any two comparative points from the list below for each part of the question.

(a) √ Monosaccharides are smaller molecules than polysaccharides.

√ Monosaccharides are soluble in water whereas polysaccharides are insoluble.

√ Monosaccharides are sweeter tasting than polysaccharides.

(b) √ Starch is made up of α-glucose molecules whereas cellulose is comprised of β-glucose molecules.

√ Cellulose has considerable structural properties; starch has not and is used as a storage material by cells.

√ Cellulose molecules are made up of unbranched chains using 1–4 glycosidic bonds; starch is made up of branched chains using both 1–4 and 1–6 glycosidic bonds.

(c) √ An unsaturated fat possesses double bonds whereas a saturated fat does not.

√ Unsaturated fats are more reactive than saturated ones.

√ Unsaturated fats are less likely to cause heart disease than saturated ones.

(d) √ Globular proteins have regular repetitive amino acid sequences whereas those of fibrous proteins are highly irregular.

√ Globular proteins have a compact shape but fibrous proteins are comprised of long chains, running parallel and linked by cross bridges.

√ Globular proteins have a relatively unstable structure whereas fibrous proteins are stable in structure.

√ Globular proteins are soluble, fibrous proteins are insoluble.

√ Globular proteins have metabolic functions, fibrous proteins have structural ones.

2. (a)

Where R may be a variety of different groups ranging from H to complex ring structures.

√√ – deduct one mark for any error.

(b) √√ Carboxyl ($-COOH$) and amino ($-NH_2$).

(c) (i)

√√√ – deduct one mark for an error.

(ii) √ Peptide bond

(iii) √ Hydrolysis

(d) √ The often spiral polypeptide chain that makes up the secondary structure is further folded and twisted in the tertiary structure.

√ The secondary structure forms as a result of hydrogen bonding, whereas the tertiary structure forms as a result of hydrogen bonding, ionic bonding and the formation of disulphide bridges.

3. (a) (i) √ Enzyme X is **not** very specific as it acts on a number of different proteins.

Enzyme Y is specific as it acts on a 'single' protein. (1 mark)

(ii) √ Enzyme X is used in biological washing powders to digest/ remove protein stains from clothes.

Enzyme Y is used in production of yoghurt/cheese from milk.

(1 mark)

(iii) √ Milk is the only food in the diet of young mammals.

√ The enzyme coagulates (solidifies) the milk, causing it to remain in the stomach and the rest of the gut for longer.

√ This gives time for it to be digested. If it had remained as a liquid it would pass through more quickly and so only be partially digested.

(iv) √ Hot springs

(b) (i) √

Temp (°C)	Time (min) for hydrolysis of protein	Rate of reaction (1/time)
15	5.8	0.17
25	3.4	0.29
35	1.7	0.59
45	0.7	1.43
55	0.6	1.67
65	0.9	1.11
75	7.1	0.14

(ii) √ Correct axes chosen.

√ Both axes correctly labelled including units.

√ Points accurately plotted.

√ Shape accurate – curve drawn through points plotted.

Marks allowed even if figures in table were inaccurately calculated, provided they are correctly plotted.

(iii) √ The optimum value is read by dropping a vertical line from the highest point on the curve and reading the temperature where it transects the temperature (x) axis. The value will depend upon how the curve has been drawn but should be in the range of 50–55°C.

(iv) √ Carry out the experiment in exactly the same way,

√ at narrower temperature intervals (e.g. 1°C)

√ over the range of 45–55°C.

4. (a) √ 1 = Microvillus

√ 2 = Smooth endoplasmic reticulum

√ 3 = Nucleus

√ 4 = Ribosome

√ 5 = Rough endoplasmic reticulum

√ 6 = Lysosome
√ 7 = Mitochondrion
√ 8 = Centriole
√ 9 = Plasma (cell) membrane
√ 10 = Golgi apparatus

(b) √ Nuclear envelope.
√   Presence of membrane bound organelles – or the naming of an example of one, e.g. mitochondrion.

(c) √ Production of glyco-proteins, by the addition of the carbohydrate portion to the protein;
√   production of secretory enzymes;
√   transport and storage of lipids;
√   formation of lysosomes.   (maximum of 3 marks)

(d) (i)   √ 6 (Lysosome)
     (ii)   √ 2 (Smooth endoplasmic reticulum)
     (iii) √ 5 (Rough endoplasmic reticulum)
     (iv)   √ 7 (Mitochondrion)
     (v)   √ 7 (Mitochondrion)

(e) √ 1 (Microvilli)
√   7 (Mitochondria)

(f) Length in diagram = 32 mm
                   1 mm = 1000 μm
               32 mm = 32 000 μm
        Magnification = 16 000

           Actual size $= \dfrac{32\,000\,\mu m}{16\,000} = \mathbf{2\,\mu m}$

Marks awarded as: √√ for workings; √ for the correct answer.

5. (a) Any two from the following for one mark each:
     (i)   √ Giving an organism a universally accepted name allows scientists to communicate about it without the risk of confusion or ambiguity.
     (ii) √ Classification indicates evolutionary relationships between organisms.
     (iii) √ It is more convenient, especially where large numbers of organisms are involved, to arrange them in a set order so that future reference is easier.   (maximum 2 marks)

    (b) √ Species; genus; family; order; class; phylum.

    (c) √ While a virus can carry out living processes such as reproduction, it can only do so by taking over the metabolic activities of a host cell, i.e. it cannot do so independently.
    √   Viruses can be crystallised, which is a non-living characteristic, rather than a living one.

6. (a) (i)   √ Resources that are, for all practical purposes, **not** replaced as they are used.
         (ii) √ Organic molecules made up of three fatty acids combined together with a glycerol molecule.
         (iii) √ A carrier, in this instance to transport DNA from one plant cell to another.

    (b) (i)   √ Energy source (heating/transport fuel).
         √   Hydrocarbon products such as plastics, polythene, detergents, resins, synthetic fibres.

(ii)   Any three of the following:

√   The supply is renewable, i.e. they can be replaced.

√   They are more biodegradable, i.e. are broken down more rapidly and leave less toxic residues.

√   They are more complex and therefore require less processing in manufacture with consequently less pollution.

√   Being derived from carbon dioxide only recently removed from the atmosphere by photosynthesis, the carbon dioxide released on their breakdown does not increase global levels and therefore does not contribute to the greenhouse effect.

(c)   √   Sucrose is broken down to glucose and fructose by sucrase.

√   The glucose and fructose is phosphorylated to give fructose bisphosphate.

√   The fructose bisphosphate (6C) is split into three two-carbon molecules (glycerate 1,3, bisphosphate).

√   The three-carbon molecule (glycerate 1,3, bisphosphate) is converted to pyruvate yielding ATP and water.

√   Pyruvate is converted to acetyl coenzyme A (2C) by the loss of CO_2 and 2H.

(d)   (i)   √ Tissues that do not normally store oil (e.g. leaves) may be damaged by its presence.

(ii)   √ Unless sufficient of the engineered oil is produced it will be swamped by the natural oils and its extraction and separation will be expensive.

4 THE CONTINUITY OF LIFE

Nucleic acids

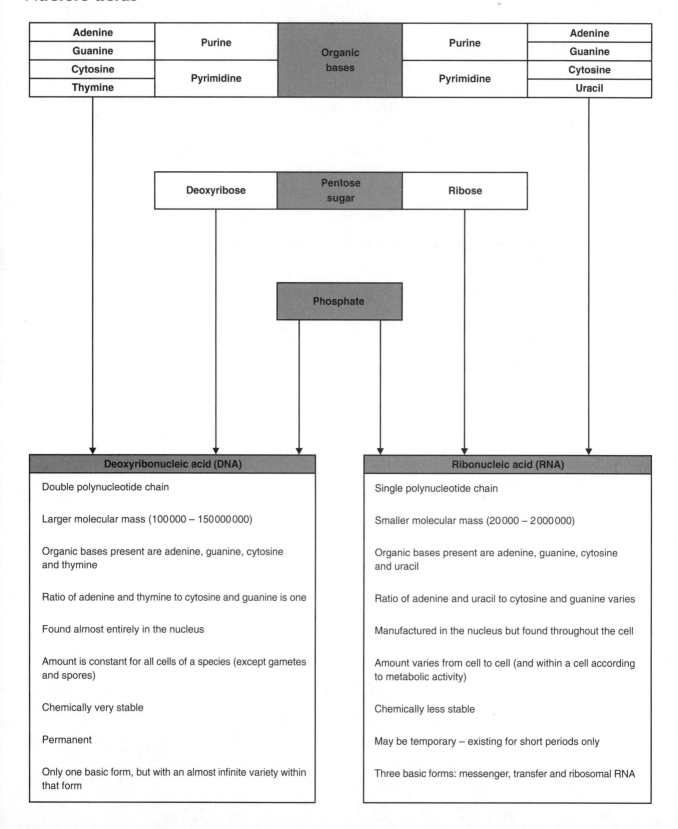

Adenine	Purine		Purine	Adenine
Guanine		Organic		Guanine
Cytosine	Pyrimidine	bases	Pyrimidine	Cytosine
Thymine				Uracil

Deoxyribose	Pentose sugar	Ribose

Phosphate

Deoxyribonucleic acid (DNA)	Ribonucleic acid (RNA)
Double polynucleotide chain	Single polynucleotide chain
Larger molecular mass (100 000 – 150 000 000)	Smaller molecular mass (20 000 – 2 000 000)
Organic bases present are adenine, guanine, cytosine and thymine	Organic bases present are adenine, guanine, cytosine and uracil
Ratio of adenine and thymine to cytosine and guanine is one	Ratio of adenine and uracil to cytosine and guanine varies
Found almost entirely in the nucleus	Manufactured in the nucleus but found throughout the cell
Amount is constant for all cells of a species (except gametes and spores)	Amount varies from cell to cell (and within a cell according to metabolic activity)
Chemically very stable	Chemically less stable
Permanent	May be temporary – existing for short periods only
Only one basic form, but with an almost infinite variety within that form	Three basic forms: messenger, transfer and ribosomal RNA

Cell division

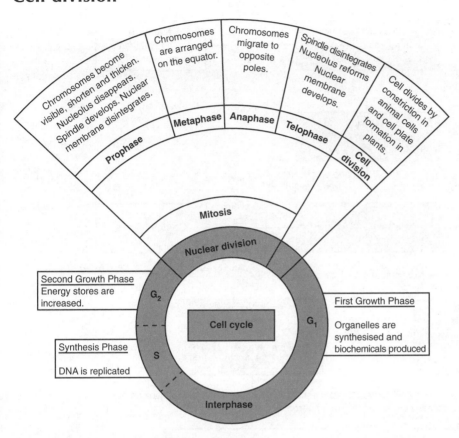

Chromosomes become visible, shorten and thicken. Nucleolus disappears. Spindle develops. Nuclear membrane disintegrates.

Prophase

Chromosomes are arranged on the equator.

Metaphase

Chromosomes migrate to opposite poles.

Anaphase

Spindle disintegrates Nucleolus reforms Nuclear membrane develops.

Telophase

Cell divides by constriction in animal cells and cell plate formation in plants.

Cell division

Mitosis

Nuclear division

Cell cycle

G₂

G₁

S

Second Growth Phase
Energy stores are increased.

First Growth Phase
Organelles are synthesised and biochemicals produced

Synthesis Phase
DNA is replicated

Interphase

Meiosis

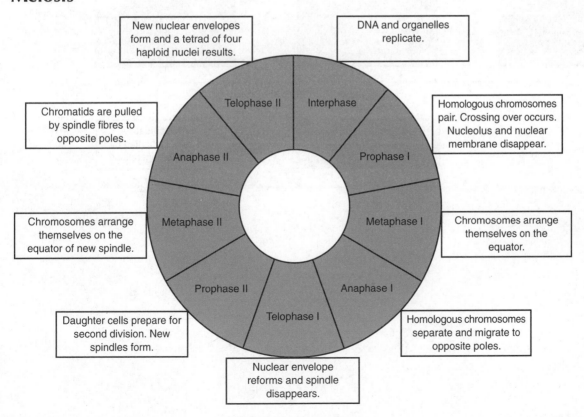

New nuclear envelopes form and a tetrad of four haploid nuclei results.

DNA and organelles replicate.

Chromatids are pulled by spindle fibres to opposite poles.

Homologous chromosomes pair. Crossing over occurs. Nucleolus and nuclear membrane disappear.

Chromosomes arrange themselves on the equator of new spindle.

Chromosomes arrange themselves on the equator.

Daughter cells prepare for second division. New spindles form.

Homologous chromosomes separate and migrate to opposite poles.

Nuclear envelope reforms and spindle disappears.

Telophase II
Interphase
Anaphase II
Prophase I
Metaphase II
Metaphase I
Prophase II
Anaphase I
Telophase I

Heredity and genetics

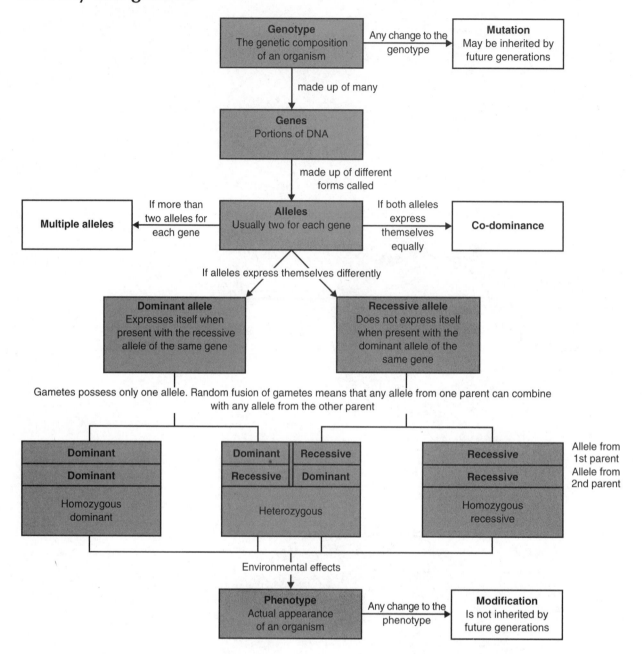

Mammalian reproduction

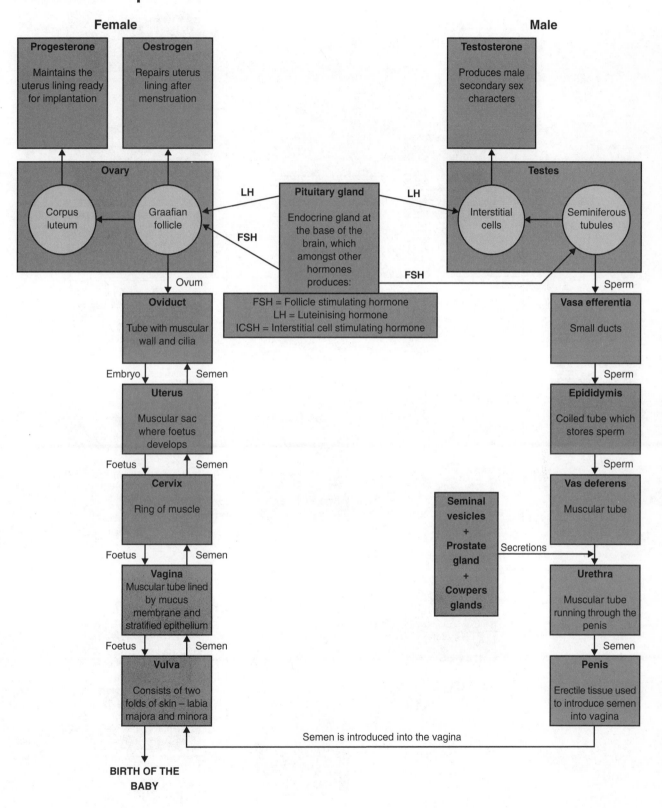

Mutations

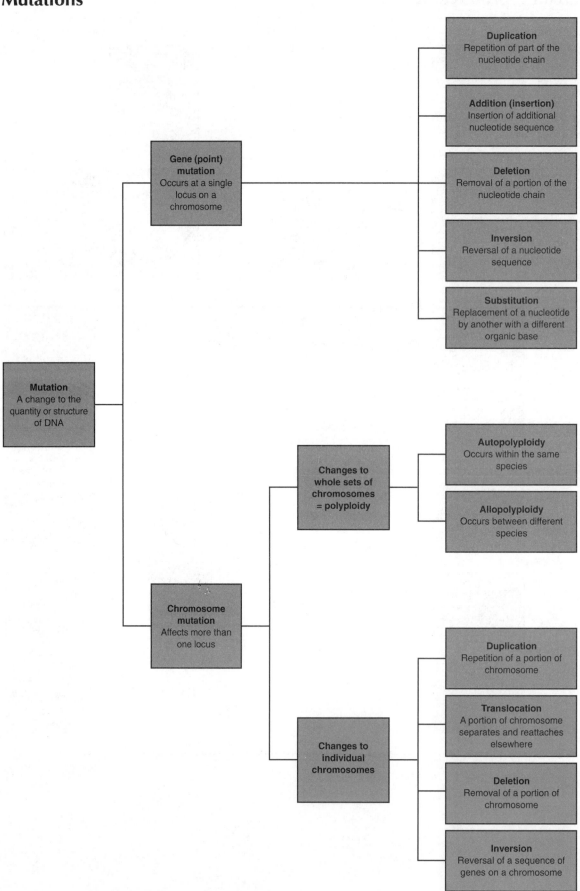

Evolution

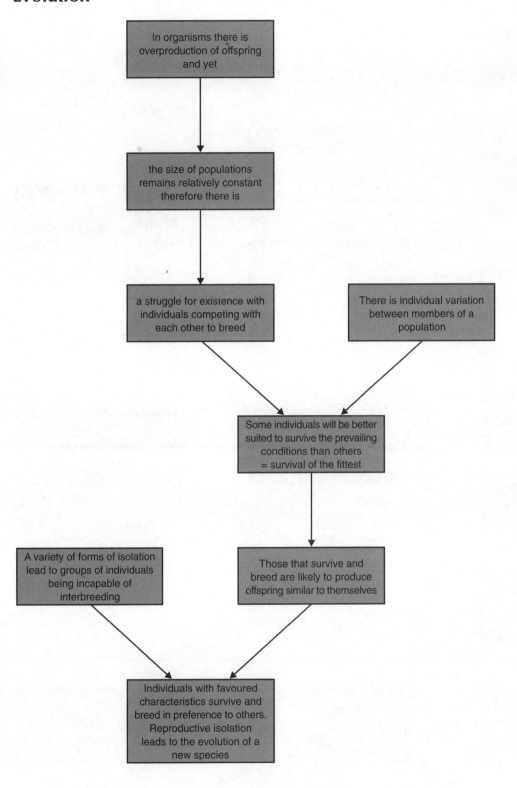

Structure of the flower

Receptacle
For attachment of
floral parts

Sepals
Protect the bud and may
photosynthesize

→

Calyx
Collective name for the
sepals

→

Perianth
Collective name for calyx
and corolla

Petals
Often brightly coloured to
attract insects

→

Corolla
Collective name for the
petals

→

Anthers
Produce pollen which contain
the male gamete

→

Stamen
Collective name for anther
and filament

→

Androecium
Collective name for all
stamens

Filaments
Hold the anthers in a
prominent position

→

Ovary
Contains ovules that enclose
the female gamete

→

Carpel
Collective name for ovary,
style and stigma

→

Gynoecium
Collective name for all
carpels

Style
Holds the stigma in a
prominent position

→

Stigma
Specialized area for
receiving pollen

Testing and applying knowledge on the continuity of life

1.   Below is a genetic code table showing the amino acids that each codon (set of three nucleotides in **mRNA**) is translated into during protein synthesis. The amino acids are indicated by three letters of its name e.g. arg = **arg**inine, ile = **i**so**le**ucine. To find the code for any amino acid you simply find the first three letters of its name on the matrix and then read off the first base in the sequence from the column on the left, the second base from the row at the top and the third base from the column to the right. You will notice that most amino acids have more than one code e.g. alanine (ala) has four codes GCU, GCC, GCA and GCG.

First position	Second position				Third position
	U	C	A	G	
U	phe	ser	tyr	cys	U
U	phe	ser	tyr	cys	C
U	leu	ser	Stop	Stop	A
U	leu	ser	Stop	trp	G
C	leu	pro	his	arg	U
C	leu	pro	his	arg	C
C	leu	pro	gin	arg	A
C	leu	pro	gin	arg	G
A	ile	thr	asn	ser	U
A	ile	thr	asn	ser	C
A	ile	thr	lys	arg	A
A	met	thr	lys	arg	G
G	val	ala	asp	gly	U
G	val	ala	asp	gly	C
G	val	ala	glu	gly	A
G	val	ala	glu	gly	G

(a)   Which **two** amino acids have only one code and what is it in each case?

(b)   Which amino acids have the following codes?
   (i)   CUC
   (ii)   AAA
   (iii)   GAU

(c)   For each of the following base sequences on a **DNA** molecule, give the sequence of amino acids in the order in which they would occur in the resultant polypeptide.
   (i)   ATG – CGT – TAA – GGC – AGT
   (ii)   GCT – AAG – TTT – CCA – GAT

(d)   A mutant form of a gene results from the inversion of the code for the amino acid glutamine (glu). What amino acid replaces the glutamine in the mutant form?

(e)   Explain the significance of the code UGA.

2.   (a) Name the point where the two chromatids of a chromosome are attached to each other.

(b)   Below is a series of statements about meiosis. In each case give the name of the stage being described, as precisely as you can.
   (i)   Homologous chromosomes arrange themselves at the equator of the cell.
   (ii)   Chromatids migrate to opposite poles.
   (iii)   Replication of DNA and organelles takes place.
   (iv)   Crossing over occurs.
   (v)   A tetrad is formed.
   (vi)   Synapsis takes place and bivalents are formed.

(c)   If the amount of DNA in a cell at the prophase stage of mitosis is 4 units, how many units of DNA are there at each of the following stages:
   (i)   Mitosis early interphase
   (ii)   Meiosis anaphase I
   (iii)   Mitosis late telophase
   (iv)   Meiosis late telophase II
   (v)   Meiosis metaphase II

3.   In the fruit fly (*Drosophila*), there is a mutant allele that causes a condition known as 'cut' wing. The table below details the wing type produced from a number of crosses:

Cross	Parents		Offspring	
	Male	Female	Male	Female
1	cut	cut	50% cut, 50% normal	100% cut
2	cut	cut	100% cut	100% cut
3	normal	normal	100% normal	100% normal
4	normal	cut	100% cut	100% cut
5	normal	cut	50% cut, 50% normal	50% cut, 50% normal
6	cut	normal	100% normal	100% cut

(a)   (i)   Do you think the mutant allele is dominant or recessive?
      (ii)   Which cross led you to this conclusion and why?

(b)   (i)   Do you think the mutant allele is autosomal or sex-linked?
      (ii)   Which cross led you to this conclusion and why?

(c)   Using B to represent the dominant allele and b to represent the recessive allele give the genotypes of the parents and offspring for the following crosses:
   (i)   Cross 1
   (ii)   Cross 5
   (iii)   Cross 6

4.   (a)   Two organisms, each heterozygous at two loci, are crossed. What proportion of the expected offspring would possess two or more dominant alleles, assuming no crossing over?

(b) State which of the following human characteristics are examples of continuous variation and which are examples of discontinuous variation: body mass, intelligence, height, blood group, skin colour.

(c) What are the chances of the male offspring of a mother carrying the gene for haemophilia being haemophiliac if his father does not have the disorder?

(d) Of the three types of selection, directional, stabilising and disruptive, which one best describes each of the following examples:

(i) A rise in environmental temperature over time leads to an increase in the length of ears in foxes.

(ii) Farmers have selected cattle to produce some breeds with horns and some without.

(iii) The increased use of antibiotics has led to the development of resistant bacteria.

(iv) More human babies with a very low or very high body mass die at birth, than ones with an average mass.

5.

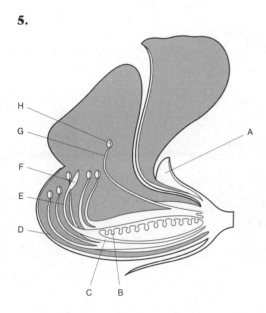

Diagram of sweet pea (Lathyrus odoratus)

State the one letter that best fits the following descriptions. Each letter may be used once, more than once or not at all.

(a) Protects the flower when in bud.
(b) Produces pollen grains.
(c) Structure down which the pollen tube grows.
(d) Where pollen must initially be deposited if fertilisation is to occur.
(e) Usually carries out photosynthesis.
(f) Possess a micropyle.
(g) As a group they form the corolla.
(h) Forms the wall of the fruit (pericarp) after fertilisation.
(i) Structures in which meiosis occurs (two answers).
(j) Has a large surface area and is often feathery in wind-pollinated plants.

6.   (a) Name the muscular tube that carries sperm from the epididymis to
the urethra.
(b) Name the structure formed once a mature Graafian follicle has
released its ovum.
(c) Which hormone causes Graafian follicles to develop in the ovary?
(d) Which hormone induces ovulation?
(e) What do the letters IVF stand for?
(f) What name is given to the process whereby a sample of fluid from
around the foetus is removed using a hypodermic needle?
(g) Which natural hormone induces birth and from where is it
produced?
(h) What term describes the type of growth whereby different organs
grow at a different rate to that of the body as a whole?

Answers to testing and applying knowledge on the continuity of life

1.   (a) **Tryp**tophase – UGG; **met**hionine – AUG

(b) (i)   **Leu**cine; (ii) **lys**ine; (iii) **asp**artate

(c) (i)   **Try**osine – **ala**nine – (**ile**)–iso**leu**cine – **pro**line – **ser**ine
(ii)   **Arg**inine – **ph**enylalanine – **lys**ine – **gly**cine – **leu**cine
NB, the DNA code must first be converted to its mRNA before
looking up the amino acids on the table.

(d) Lysine (because GAA becomes AAG – the reversal of GAG has no
effect because it still codes for glutamine).

(e) UGA is a 'stop' or 'nonsense' code that signifies the end of an
amino acid sequence at which point the polypeptide is complete and
is cast off.

2.   (a) Centromere

(b) (i)   metaphase I; (ii) anaphase II; (iii) interphase; (iv) prophase I;
(v)   telophase II; (vi) prophase I.

(c) (i) 2; (ii) 4; (iii) 2; (iv) 1; (v) 2.

3.   (a) (i)   Dominant
(ii)   EITHER: Cross 1 because if the cut allele were recessive, all the
offspring would have cut wings, but in fact some normal offspring
are produced, OR: Cross 4, because where one parent has cut wings
and one normal wings, **all** the offspring have cut wings.

(b) (i)   Sex-linked
(ii)   EITHER: Cross 1, OR: Cross 6, because the ratio of cut to
normal wings differs greatly between males and females.

(c) (i)   Parents – male = $X^B Y$;   female = $X^B X^b$
Offspring – $X^B X^B, X^B X^b, X^B Y, X^b Y$.
(ii)   Parents – male = $X^b Y$;   female = $X^B X^b$
Offspring – $X^B X^b, X^b X^b, X^B Y, X^b Y$.
(iii) Parents – male = $X^B Y$;   female = $X^b X^b$
Offspring – $X^B X^b, X^b Y$.

4. (a) $\frac{11}{16}$.

(b) Blood groups are an example of discontinuous variation – all others display continuous variation.

(c) One in two / 50% chance / 0.5.

(d) (i) Directional
(ii) Disruptive
(iii) Directional
(iv) Stabilising

5. (a) A; (b) H; (c) E; (d) F; (e) A; (f) B; (g) D; (h) C; (i) B and H; (j) F.

6. (a) Vas deferens
(b) Corpus luteum
(c) Follicle stimulating hormone (FSH)
(d) Luteinising hormone (LH)
(e) *In vitro* fertilisation
(f) Amniocentesis
(g) Oxytocin produced by the posterior lobe of the pituitary gland.
(h) Allometric growth

Sample question on the continuity of life

Coat colour in rabbits is determined by multiple alleles. Chinchilla coat (c^{ch}) is dominant to Himalayan coat (c^h). The allele for full coat colour (C) is dominant to both these, whereas the albino allele (c) is recessive to all the others.

The inheritance of coat colour follows normal Mendelian principles for autosomal genes.

(a) What is meant by 'multiple alleles'? (*2 marks*)

(b) State the number of alleles for coat colour that would be found in each somatic cell of an individual rabbit. (*1 mark*)

(c) List all possible genotypes for the following rabbits:
(i) Heterozygous for full coat
(ii) Homozygous for Himalayan coat
(iii) Heterozygous for chinchilla coat

(*6 marks*)

(d) What offspring phenotypic ratios would be expected from the following crosses:
(i) $c^h c^{ch} \times c^h c^{ch}$
(ii) $Cc \times c^h c^{ch}$ (*4 marks*)

(e) A breeder suspects his chinchilla buck is not homozygous at the C locus and so mates it with a pure-breeding Himalayan doe. He obtains a litter of seven chinchilla rabbits only. How certain could he be that his buck is homozygous at the C locus? (*7 marks*)

(*Total 20 marks*)

Guided response to sample question on the continuity of life

(a)   The two marks for stating what is meant by multiple alleles are likely to be distributed as follows:
√ A set of **more than two** alleles
√ at a **single** locus on a chromosome.

(b)   If you consider that there are always two chromosome sets in a sexually reproducing organism (one derived from each parent), it follows that, however many **possible** alleles there may be, there can only ever be **two** (√) present at any one time in somatic cells.

(c)   (i)   To have a full coat, the allele C must be present. The second allele must however be **different** as we are asked for 'heterozygous' genotypes. Because C is dominant to all others, then any of the remaining three can be the second allele, giving the answers:
√ Cc^{ch}
√ Cc^{h}
√ Cc
(ii)   For the coat to be Himalayan it must possess the Himalayan coat allele – c^{h}. As we are asked for the **homozygous** genotype both alleles must be the same, namely:
√$c^{h}c^{h}$
(iii)   For a rabbit to have a chinchilla coat, it must possess the c^{ch} allele but not the C allele, as this is dominant and would express itself in the phenotype at the expense of the chinchilla allele – c^{ch}. The chinchilla allele can, however, be present with either of the alleles that are recessive to it – namely c^{h} or c. It cannot however be present with a second c^{ch} allele as this would make it homozygous rather than heterozygous as required. The answers are therefore:
√$c^{ch}c^{h}$
√$c^{ch}c$

(d)   Many marks are lost needlessly in answers to genetic questions, because the reader is unable to follow the working due to messy presentation or poor labelling. Always lay out the answer logically, clearly and with labels for guidance. The use of Punnett squares is especially helpful and less prone to error. It is important in both answers that the 'phenotypes' and their ratios are given as asked – it is all too easy to simply leave the genotypes without describing their appearance. The answers, with likely points where marks can be credited, are given below.

(i)   **Parent 1**   **Parent 2**

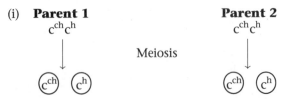

Parent 1 gametes

		c^{ch}	c^{h}
Parent 2	c^{ch}	$c^{ch}c^{ch}$	$c^{ch}c^{h}$
gametes	c^{h}	$c^{ch}c^{h}$	$c^{h}c^{h}$

Genotypes **Phenotypes**

$\sqrt{}\ 1 \times c^{ch}c^{ch} + 2 \times c^{ch}c^h\ =\ $ 3 chinchilla coat

$1\ c^hc^h\ =\ $ 1 Himalayan coat

$\sqrt{}$ Phenotypic ratio = 3 chinchilla coat : 1 Himalayan coat

(ii) **Parent 1** **Parent 2**

Cc $c^{ch}c^{ch}$

↓ Meiosis ↓

Ⓒ ⓒ Ⓒ^{ch} Ⓒ^{h}

Parent 1 gametes

		Ⓒ	ⓒ
Parent 2	Ⓒ^{ch}	Cc^{ch}	$c^{ch}c$
gametes	Ⓒ^{h}	Cc^h	c^hc

Genotypes **Phenotypes**

$\sqrt{}$ $Cc^{ch} + Cc^h$ = 2 full coat

$c^{ch}c$ = 1 chinchilla coat

c^hc = 1 Himalayan coat

$\sqrt{}$ Phenotypic ratio = 2 full coats:1 chinchilla coat:1 Himalayan coat

(e) Start your answer with the information that you can be sure of – in this case the genotype of the Himalayan-coated doe, must be c^hc^h ($\sqrt{}$), as it is pure breeding (i.e. homozygous). The chinchilla-coated buck, however, has three possible genotypes. It may either be homozygous and therefore $c^{ch}c^{ch}$ or, as the breeder suspects, heterozygous in which case there are two possibilities namely $c^{ch}c^h$ or $c^{ch}c$.

If homozygous then the offspring will **all** have chinchilla coats as shown:

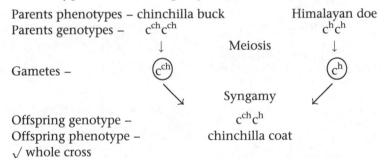

Parents phenotypes – chinchilla buck Himalayan doe
Parents genotypes – $c^{ch}c^{ch}$ c^hc^h

↓ Meiosis ↓

Gametes – Ⓒ^{ch} Ⓒ^{h}

Syngamy

Offspring genotype – $c^{ch}c^h$
Offspring phenotype – chinchilla coat
$\sqrt{}$ whole cross

If the buck with a chinchilla coat is heterozygous, then of the offspring, half have chinchilla coats and half have Himalayan coats whichever of the two heterozygous genotypes is present:

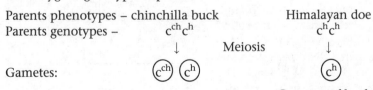

Parents phenotypes – chinchilla buck Himalayan doe
Parents genotypes – $c^{ch}c^h$ c^hc^h

↓ Meiosis ↓

Gametes: Ⓒ^{ch} Ⓒ^{h} Ⓒ^{h}

Gametes of buck

		Ⓒ^{ch}	Ⓒ^{h}
Gametes of doe	Ⓒ^{h}	$c^{ch}c^h$	c^hc^h

1 : 1 chinchilla : Himalayan
$c^{ch}c^h$ c^hc^h

$\sqrt{}\sqrt{}$: whole cross

Parents phenotypes – chinchilla buck   Himalayan doe
Parents genotypes – $c^{ch}c$ c^hc^h

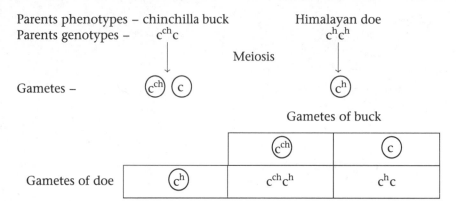

TUTORIAL TIP

It is essential in genetics questions to show **all** working, so that if an error is made which gives the wrong answer, some credit can nevertheless be given providing the working is consistent with the error and follows accepted genetic principles.

1 : 1 chinchilla : Himalayan
      $c^{ch}c^h$ c^hc
$\sqrt{}\sqrt{}$: whole cross

In both cases the probability of getting a chinchilla rabbit $= \frac{1}{2}$. Hence with a litter of seven chinchillas the breeder could expect three or four Himalayans if his buck was heterozygous. It is therefore more likely that it is actually homozygous, which would produce all chinchilla rabbits ($\sqrt{}$). A more discerning candidate may like to put a figure on this probability. The probability of getting one chinchilla rabbit if his buck was heterozygous $= \frac{1}{2}$. The chances of getting seven is therefore $(\frac{1}{2})^7 = \frac{1}{128}$. Since the probability of being either heterozygous or homozygous $= 1$ (certainty), the chances of being homozygous must be $1 - \frac{1}{128} = \frac{127}{128} = 99.2\%$ certain. $\sqrt{}$ (bonus).

Practice questions on the continuity of life

Q. 1

The following is an account of DNA structure and protein synthesis. Complete the passage by providing the most appropriate word for each of the numbered spaces.

DNA is made up of a sugar called ...(1)... , phosphate units and four different ...(2)... bases. The bases occur in pairs held together by ...(3)... bonds. The base called cytosine is always paired with one called ...(4)... , while thymine is always paired with ...(5)... . Cytosine and thymine belong to a group of bases called ...(6)... . The DNA is rather like a ladder with the sugar and phosphate units making the uprights and the organic bases forming the rungs. This ladder is twisted to form a ...(7)... . The two strands forming the uprights run in opposite directions and are therefore said to be ...(8)... . In each complete turn of this twisted ladder there are ...(9)... base pairings. In protein synthesis DNA forms a template known as ...(10)... RNA, which has a different sugar, known as ...(11)... . Another difference is that RNA has an organic base called ...(12)... in place of the base called ...(13)... found in DNA. The template is stored for a short time in the ...(14)... before moving out into the cytoplasm and becoming associated with organelles called ...(15)... . In the cytoplasm are smaller strands of RNA called ...(16).... RNA, each of which joins up with a specific ...(17)... at one end; at the other end is a total of ...(18)... organic bases known as an ...(19)... . These bases join up with a complementary set of bases called the ...(20)..., which occurs on the template. The amino acids become joined in a chain by ...(21)... bonds that result in a molecule called a ...(22)... .

TUTORIAL TIP

When completing a 'missing words' passage, it is a good idea to read through the whole passage first to get an overall view of the whole paragraph, and again at the end to ensure the whole thing is logical and accurate.

(22 marks)

Q. 2

(a)   Distinguish between cell and nuclear division.   (*3 marks*)

(b)   What are the advantages and disadvantages for an organism in having meiotic divisions as part of its life cycle, compared with one that reproduces only by mitosis?   (*10 marks*)

(c)   Four organisms found on a previously undiscovered and isolated island were investigated for the number of chromosomes found in their cells. The results were as follows:

Organism	Individual	No. of cells	Chromosome no.
Lanky grobe	A	Almost all cells	16
		A few cells	8
Speckled bobbit	A	All cells	39
	B	All cells	38
Dosey fleck	A	All cells	16
	B	All cells	12
	C	All cells	8
Slippery toot	A	All cells	17

In each case provide an explanation for the different number of chromosomes found in the cells and give an example of a corresponding situation in the human biological world.   (*12 marks*)

(*Total 25 marks*)

TUTORIAL TIP

The relatively large allocation of 10 marks for part (b) indicates that a detailed explanation is needed.

Q. 3

M and N are two antigens that occur in the blood. When a population of 416 individuals were tested for the presence of these alleles the results were as follows:

Antigen(s) present	No. of individuals
M only	238
N only	26
Both	152

Assuming that the presence of MN antigens is the result of the inheritance of one pair of alleles, calculate the frequencies of the two alleles and expected Hardy–Weinberg genotypic ratios. Is the population in Hardy–Weinberg equilibrium?

(*Total 10 marks*)

TUTORIAL TIP

You will need to know the Hardy–Weinberg formula to answer this question.

TUTORIAL TIP

Remember that alleles occur in pairs and therefore individuals with the M antigen only have two alleles for that antigen – they are MM. The same applies to the N allele. Those with both antigens are MN.

Q. 4

The graph below shows the variation in the mean diameter of follicles and corpora lutea in the ovary of a pig during a 40-day period.

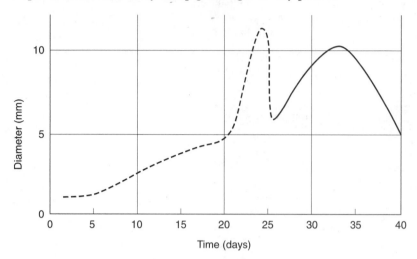

(a) (i)   What is the name of the hormone that causes the follicles to begin to increase in size around day 6?   (*1 mark*)
(ii) Between which days do you think the introduction of sperm is most likely to result in fertilisation? Give reasons for your answer.
                                                                                                     (*4 marks*)
(iii) Giving a reason for your answer say on which day you think ovulation took place.   (*2 marks*)
(iv) What evidence supports the view that fertilisation did not take place?   (*1 mark*)

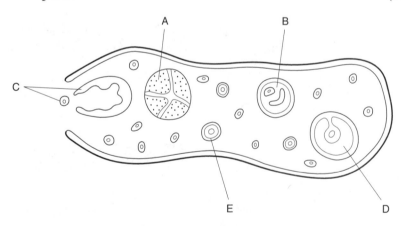

Section through a mammalian ovary

(b) (i)   Name the parts labelled A, B, C, D and E.   (*5 marks*)
(ii) State the correct developmental sequence of these five structures.
                                                                                                     (*3 marks*)

(c) State whether each of the following is diploid or haploid:
(i)   germinal epithelium
(ii) ovum
(iii) secondary oocyte
(iv) primary oocyte   (*4 marks*)
                                                                                (*Total 20 marks*)

> **TUTORIAL TIP**
>
> The 4 marks allocated in (a) (ii) are likely to be 1 for the correct day and 3 for the reasons — suggesting that three reasons are required.

> **TUTORIAL TIP**
>
> In (c) place the four structures in their correct developmental sequence and then decide when in that sequence meiosis occurs. All structures prior to meiosis will be diploid, those after it — haploid, until fertilisation occurs.

THE CONTINUITY OF LIFE

Q. 5

Read through the following passage and then, using the information it contains and your own biological knowledge, answer the questions below.

Over the last few years, a process called 'fluorescence *in situ*
hybridisation' (FISH) has been developed. This enables researchers
to 'paint' chromosomes or parts of chromosomes and their genes. This
chromosome painting technique has been used for many plant and
animal species. It can, for example, differentiate between chromo- 5
somes derived from different parents, detect translocations, sites
of recombination and even individual gene sequences.

To illustrate 'chromosome painting' let us use an example of
plants with high and low protein levels (we will call them plants A
and B for convenience). We want to follow the progress of the chromo- 10
somes from the high-protein line (A) in the hybrid between plants A
and B, and their subsequent offspring. To do this, we tag (label)
all the DNA from the nucleus (the genomic DNA) of one parent (A in
our example) with a fluorescent die and then hybridise (bind) this
labelled DNA onto the corresponding segments of DNA in the chromo- 15
somes of our hybrid plant AB.

First we extract the DNA from one parent (parent A), and break it up
by squeezing it through a hypodermic needle or by zapping it with
ultrasound. The fragments of DNA are then treated with a solution
of enzymes and nucleotides - the building blocks of nucleic acids. 20
One of the enzymes is DNAse 1, which makes random breaks or 'nicks'
in the DNA. Another enzyme, DNA polymerase 1, then rebuilds the
nucleotides on the broken pieces, using the nucleotides we have
added, one of which carries the fluorescent label. The rebuilt DNA
fragments are thus labelled with a fluorescent dye (the 'paint') 25
and are known as probe DNA.

Having made our paint, we now need a canvas on which to paint, chromosomes of the hybrid plant AB. To make a chromosome canvas we take
root tips from germinated seed of our hybrid and then treat them in
ice-cold water to contract the chromosomes and to cause cells to 30
accumulate at the metaphase stage of mitotic division. They are
then squashed onto a microscope slide and allowed to dry. The
canvas is now ready.

There are various methods of applying the 'paint', but they all
involve the same general principle. Under normal circumstances, DNA 35
is **double-stranded** but can be denatured (separated into single
strands) by heat and chemical treatments. If the denatured DNA is
then allowed to cool, the two strands bind together to become
double-stranded. Thus, if we add denatured, single-stranded,
labelled probe DNA (the paint) to the denatured chromosome DNA on 40
the microscope slide (the canvas) and allow it to cool, the probe
DNA sticks (re-anneals) onto any complementary sequence it finds on
the chromosomes to become double-stranded again. The chromosomes or
parts of chromosomes derived from parent A now carry a fluorescent
label. To provide contrast to the picture, an 'overcoat' or coun- 45
ter-stain is also applied to the microscope slide, which stains all
the chromosomes (blue in our case), regardless of their origins.

Now that the painting is complete, we look at the slide using a
fluorescent microscope. This instrument allows us to vary the wavelength of light such that at one wavelength only the overcoat will 50
fluoresce. At a second wavelength, only the labelled or 'painted'
parts of the chromosomes fluoresce. The two images can be combined
in a photograph by taking a double exposure of the cell at two

different wavelengths. Now, all the chromosomes or parts of chromosomes derived from parent A are coloured red – the chromosomes or   55
parts of chromosomes from parent B are coloured blue.

We find that the chromosomes derived from parent A are mainly red,
and those from parent B are mainly blue, but the ends of some of the
red chromosomes are blue, and vice versa. These different coloured
ends indicate that 'swaps' have taken place between the A and B   60
chromosomes of the parents. By studying these 'swaps', we can
follow what happens to chromosomes (and hence genes) from generation
to generation or from hybrid to hybrid.

> From an article 'Chromosome Painting' by Mike Leggett in the
> *Biological Sciences Review*, Vol. 8, No. 4.

(a)   Explain what is meant by each of the following terms:
    (i)   'translocations' (line 6)   (*1 mark*)
    (ii) 'sites of recombination' (lines 6 and 7)   (*1 mark*)
    (iii) 'nucleotides' (line 23)   (*1 mark*)

(b)   Suggest a possible useful application of chromosome painting in
humans.   (*1 mark*)

(c)   Explain how 'heat and chemical treatment' (line 37) can cause DNA to
be separated into its two strands.   (*3 marks*)

(d)   (i)   What advantage could there be in 'following the progress of the
      chromosomes from the high protein line in the hybrid and their
      subsequent offspring' (lines 10 to 12)?   (*2 marks*)
    (ii) In the absence of chromosome painting, suggest another method
    by which the progress of these chromosomes could be followed?
                                                                    (*1 mark*)
                                                              (*Total 10 marks*)

Answers to practice questions on the continuity of life

1.   √ One mark for each correct word in bold.

DNA is made up of a sugar called **deoxyribose**, phosphate units and four
different **organic** bases. The bases occur in pairs held together by **hydrogen** bonds. The base called cytosine is always paired with one called
guanine, while thymine is always paired with **adenine**. Cytosine and
thymine belong to a group of bases called **pyrimidines**. The DNA is
rather like a ladder with the sugar and phosphate units making the uprights
and the organic bases forming the rungs. This ladder is twisted to form a
helix. The two strands forming the uprights run in opposite directions
and are therefore said to be **antiparallel**. In each complete turn of this
twisted ladder there are **ten** base pairings. In protein synthesis DNA forms
a template known as **messenger** RNA, which has a different sugar, known
as **ribose**. Another difference is that RNA has an organic base called
uracil in place of the base called **thymine** found in DNA. The template
is stored for a short time in the **nucleus/nucleoplasm** before moving
out into the cytoplasm and becoming associated with organelles called
ribosomes. In the cytoplasm are smaller strands of RNA called **transfer**
RNA each of which joins up with a specific **amino acid** at one end; at the
other end is a total of **three** organic bases known as an **anticodon**.
These bases join up with a complementary set of bases called the **codon**
which occurs on the template. The amino acids become joined in a chain
by **peptide** bonds which result in a molecule called a **polypeptide**.

2. (a) Any three from the following for one mark each:

Cell division	Nuclear division
√ Different in plants and animals (cell plate vs constriction)	Similar in plants and animals
√ Daughter cells always similar	Daughter nuclei may be similar (mitosis) or dissimilar (meiosis)
√ Duplication of cell organelles	Duplication of chromosomes
√ Preceded by nuclear division	Not always followed by cell division (i.e. may form multinucleate cell)
√ No spindle formed	Spindle formed

(b) **Advantages of meiotic division**

There is an increased variation of offspring possible as a result of:

√ crossing over during prophase I;

√ independent assortment of chromosomes during metaphase I;

√ formation of haploid gametes, which can then combine in many different pairs to give new genotypes.

√ If two combining gametes are both recessive, this allele can express itself in the offspring.

√ Variation provides a range of individuals upon which selection can operate and so lead to evolutionary change.

Disadvantages of meiotic division

√ The process is complex and complicated mechanisms are needed to ensure effective mating and fertilisation.

√ There is a greater risk of mutations occurring, the majority of which are harmful.

Advantages of mitosis

√ Numbers of offspring can be built up rapidly allowing favourable conditions to be rapidly exploited.

√ By producing identical offspring, successful genotypes can be cloned and the numbers of these successful genes can be built up in the gene pool.

√ There is a much smaller risk of mutations.

Disadvantages of mitosis

√ There is little if any opportunity for variety because there is no recombination of DNA or exchange of genetic material.

√ This means there is almost no scope for adapting to environmental change and so no potential for evolutionary development.

(maximum 10 marks)

(c) √√√ **Lanky grobe** – organism A uses meiosis as part of its life cycle. The majority of cells have a diploid number of chromosomes (16 in this case) but a few cells, e.g. the gametes, have undergone meiosis and so are haploid, i.e. have half the number of chromosomes in a few cells (in this case 8). Known examples include most sexually reproducing organisms, e.g. humans.

√√√ **Speckled bobbit** – this organism has two separate types; one with the normal complement of chromosomes – namely 38, the other with an additional chromosome, probably the result of non-disjunction during meiosis. The situation occurs in Down's syndrome where children have 47 rather than the usual 46 chromosomes. It is not the case that 39 is the normal number and the other variety has a chromosome missing because all fertile organisms have paired chromosomes and so the diploid number is even.

√√√ **Dosey fleck** – this could be an example of polyploidy. The haploid number is four, making specimen C diploid (8 chromosomes), specimen B triploid (12 chromosomes) and specimen A tetraploid (16 chromosomes). This situation is rare in animals, but not uncommon in plants e.g. wheat.

√√√ **Slippery toot** – while all fertile organisms have a diploid number which is even, there are infertile hybrids that can arise from cross-breeding between two species. In this case it could be a cross between organisms whose diploid numbers are 16 and 18. The gametes will possess 8 and 9 chromosomes respectively, which on fusing give an infertile hybrid with 17 chromosomes. An example is the mule (2n = 63) as the result of a cross between a horse (2n = 60) and a donkey (2n = 66).

Three marks for each organism, i.e. 2 for the explanation and 1 for an appropriate example.

3.   √ Hardy–Weinberg is expressed as: $p^2 + 2pq + q^2 = 1$
√ (where p and q = the respective frequencies of the dominant and recessive alleles).
√ Genetically this is represented as: MM + 2MN + NN = 1 (100%) (i.e. the whole of the population must be one or other of the three genotypes).
√ From the table we know that the number of individuals of each type are:

MM	MN	NN	Total
238	152	26	416

√ The number of each allele is therefore:
M = (238 × 2) + 152 = 628
N = (26 × 2) + 152 = 204
            Total = 832
(i.e. double the number of people in the population because each person has two alleles.)

√ The frequency of M (p) is therefore $\dfrac{628}{832} = 0.76$

√ The frequency of N (q) is therefore $\dfrac{204}{832} = 0.24$

√ This shows that the M allele is almost exactly three times more common than the N allele.
√ The genotype ratios are therefore:
For the MM genotype $= p^2 \quad = 0.76 \times 0.76 = \mathbf{0.58}$
For the MN genotype $= 2pq = 2 \times 0.76 \times 0.76 \times 0.24 = \mathbf{0.36}$
For the NN genotype $= q^2 \quad = 0.24 \times 0.24 = \mathbf{0.06}$
√ The expected numbers of each genotype are therefore:
    MM – 0.58 × 416 = 242
    MN – 0.36 × 416 = 150
    NN – 0.06 × 416 = 24
√ This ratio of 242:150:24 is very close to the observed ratio of 238:152:26 and the population is therefore in Hardy–Weinberg equilibrium.

4.   (a)   (i)   √ Follicle stimulating hormone.   (1 mark)
              (ii)   √ Between days 21 and 27
                     √ because the egg is released on day 24 (when the diameter of the follicle is suddenly reduced) and
                     √ sperm typically live for up to 3 days and so those introduced on day 21 could still be able to fertilise the egg released on day 24.
                     √ The egg typically takes 3 days to reach the uterus and so could still be fertilised as late as day 27.

                                                        (4 marks as shown)

(iii) √ On day 25

√ because there is a sudden decrease in the size of the follicle / the follicle changes into the corpus luteum at this point.

(iv) √ The corpus luteum does not develop further / reduces in diameter.

(b) (i) √ A – Corpus luteum

√ B – Primary oocyte (surrounded by follicle cells)

√ C – Ovum being released from Graafian follicle

√ D – Mature Graafian follicle

√ E – Primary follicle

(ii) The primary follicle (E) is present in the ovary at birth. After puberty it may mature into a primary oocyte (B) and later into a Graafian follicle (D). The ovum from this Graafian follicle is released at ovulation (C) and the empty follicle develops into the corpus luteum (A).

√√√ The sequence is hence E, B, D, G, A.

Deduct one mark for each occasion where the next stage does not correctly follow its predecessor.

(c) (i) diploid

(ii) haploid

(iii) haploid

(iv) diploid

5. (a) (i) √ A portion of chromosome becomes deleted and rejoins at a different point on the same chromosome or as part of a different chromosome.

(ii) √ The points (chiasmata) at which chromatids of homologous chromosomes break and recombine with a different chromatid so exchanging genetic material.

(iii) √ A combination of phosphoric acid, a pentose sugar and an organic base; nucleotides are the basic units of which the nucleic acids, RNA and DNA are made.

(b) √ It could be used to detect numerical and structural abnormalities of chromosomes (e.g. Prader–Willi syndrome – a form of mental retardation caused by a chromosome deletion).

(c) √ The two strands of DNA are held together by hydrogen bonds between complementary base pairs.

√ Heat increases the kinetic energy of the DNA strands causing them to vibrate thus breaking these weak hydrogen bonds.

√ Certain chemicals (e.g. acids and alkalis) may combine with a radical so preventing it combining with its opposite radical on the other organic base thus breaking the hydrogen bond.

(d) (i) √ Knowing which plants have the relevant chromosome allows selective breeding to increase the protein content of plants.

√ High-protein yielding plants have greater nutritive value and hence may be economically more important.

(ii) √ By carrying out a chemical analysis of each individual plant to determine its protein content.

5 ENERGETICS

Autotrophic nutrition (Photosynthesis)

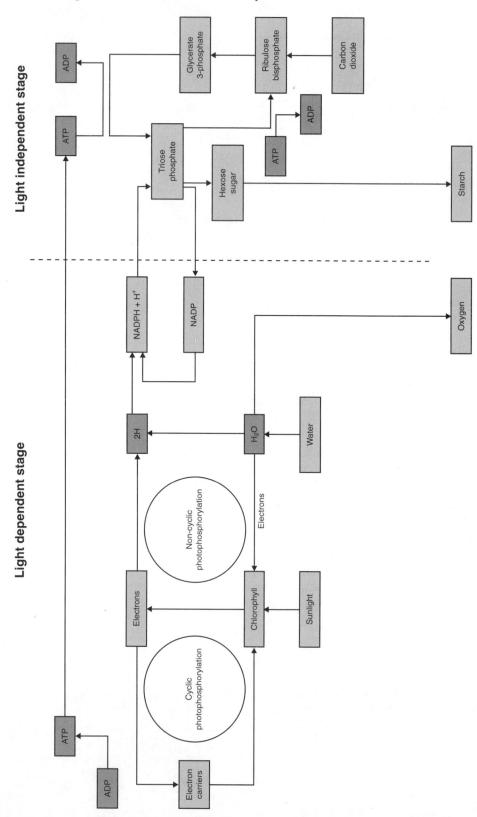

Heterotrophic nutrition in mammals

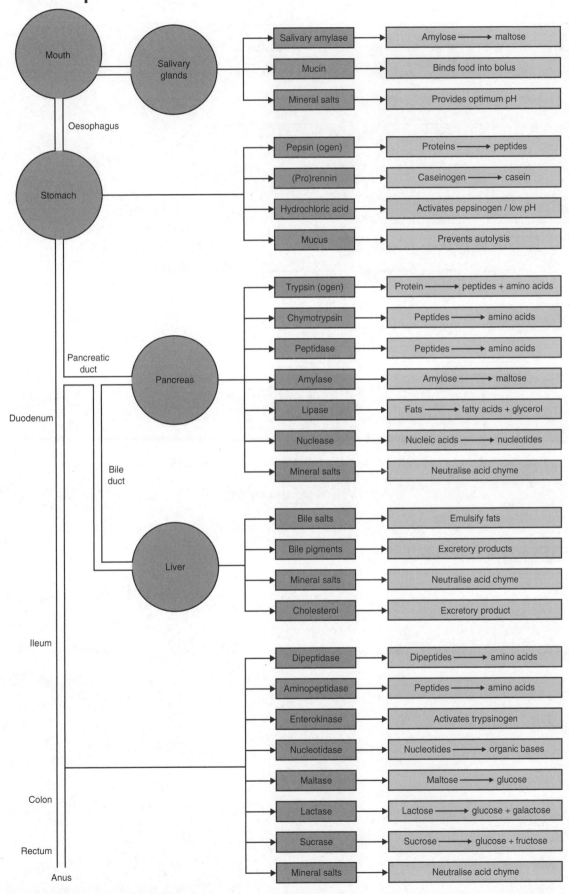

Pathways in cellular respiration

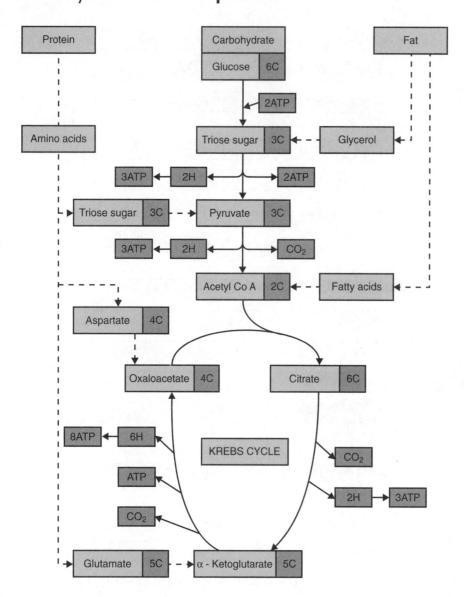

Energy flow in the ecosystem

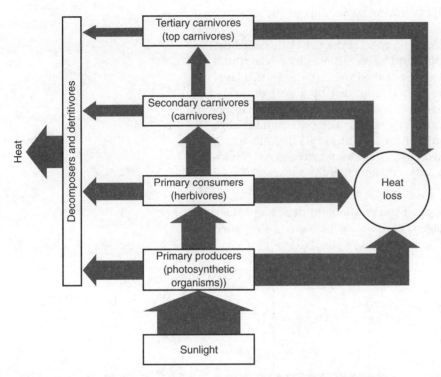

(Size of arrows gives some indication of relative amounts of energy – but they are not to scale)

Testing and applying knowledge on energetics

1. (a) Complete the blanks in the following passage about the structure and function of a leaf:

A leaf is made up of the stalk called the ...(A)... and a flat blade called the ...(B).... It is bounded on both upper and lower surfaces by a waterproof ...(C)... which covers a single-celled layer called the ...(D).... In this layer are pores called ...(E)... each of which is bounded by a pair of ...(F)... [2 words]. The main site of photosynthesis in the leaf is a layer of closely fitted elongated cells called the ...(G)... [2 words]. The cells contain large numbers of ...(H)... which trap sunlight in structures called grana which are made up of flattened sacs called ...(I).... The water needed for photosynthesis is brought to the leaf in ...(J)... tissue while the sugars produced are carried away by the ...(K)....

(b) Photosynthesis has two distinct stages, the light dependent stage and the light independent stage. The diagram below is a simplified sequence of the light independent stage:

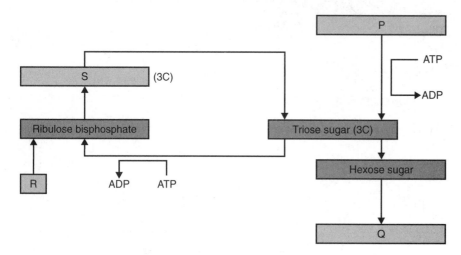

(i) Name the substances P, Q, R and S.
(ii) How many carbon atoms has ribulose bisphosphate?
(iii) From which intermediate may amino acids be synthesised?
(iv) Which **two** intermediates are needed to form fats?
(v) What are the products of the light dependent stage?

(c) (i) What is meant by the term 'action spectrum' in relation to photosynthesis?
(ii) Give the colour and approximate wavelength of the two bands of light that give the maximum rate of photosynthesis.
(iii) Give the name and colour of **four** pigments normally found in a chloroplast.

2. (a) From the following list of dietary substances, choose the one that most closely fits the descriptions below. Each substance may be used once, more than once, or not at all.

A – Calcium   B – Vitamin D (calciferol)
C – Dietary fibre   D – Iodine
E – Vitamin C (ascorbic acid)   F – Amino acids
G – Vitamin B₁ (thiamin)   H – Lipids
I – Phosphate   J – Iron

(i) Found in meat and green vegetables, it is an important component of haemoglobin.

(ii)   Its absence in the diet, causes a nervous disorder called beri beri.

(iii) A component of growth hormone, thyroxine.

(iv) Needed in large quantities for growth and repair.

(v)   An essential part of teeth and bones, it is also needed if blood is to clot properly.

(vi) Can be produced by the action of sunlight on the skin.

(vii) Needed to form collagen fibres, lemons are a major source of it.

(viii) A constituent of DNA.

(ix) Found in cod-liver oil its absence in the diet causes rickets.

(x)   Part of the cell membrane, but not found in teeth.

(b) Complete the table below by indicating the most appropriate word(s) to replace the numbers.

Name of enzyme	Source of enzyme	Substrate	Product(s)
(1)	Intestinal wall	Maltose	(2)
Rennin	(3)	(4)	(5)
(6)	(7)	(8)	Glucose and fructose
(9)	Salivary glands	(10)	(11)
Aminopeptidase	(12)	(13)	(14)
Chymotrypsin	(15)	(16)	(17)
(18)	(19)	(20)	Fatty acids + glycerol

3.   The following diagram outlines the stages of cellular respiration in organisms.

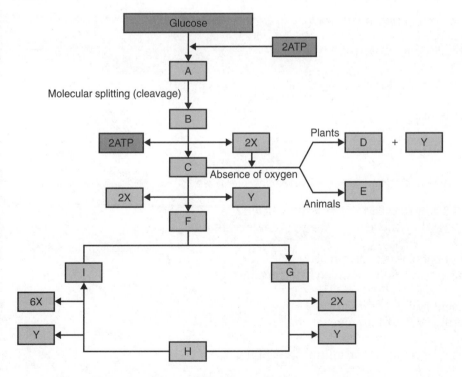

(a) (i)   What name is given to the sequence of reactions involving compounds A–C?

(ii) Where in the cell does this process take place?

(iii) Name the compound A.

(iv) What is the general name for the type of reaction illustrated by the formation of A from glucose using ATP?

(b) Name the compounds:
(i)   C; (ii) D; (iii) E.
(iv) What general name is given to the anaerobic process by which D and E are produced?

(c) Name the compounds:
(i)   F; (ii) G; (iii) H; (iv) I.
(v) What name is given to the sequence of reactions involving compounds F–I?
(vi) Where in the cell do these reactions take place?

(d) (i)   What chemical does the letter X represent?
(ii) Give the name of the compound that *initially* carries X.
(iii) X is passed along a pathway of carriers in order to yield energy (ATP). What is the final acceptor of X at the end of this pathway?
(iv) What enzyme catalyses this final removal of X from the pathway?
(v) Name an inhibitor of this enzyme, which is therefore a potentially lethal substance.

(e) Using the letters on the diagram, identify the following:
(i)   A two-carbon molecule.
(ii) A five-carbon molecule.
(iii) A six-carbon molecule more likely to be found in mitochondria than cytoplasm.
(iv) A compound that causes cramp if it accumulates in muscles.
(v) The point where fatty acids may enter the respiratory pathway.
(vi) A three-carbon atom with a phosphate group.
(vii) A compound that is released as a gas.

4. (a) The following is a list of terms:
A – Ecology
B – Conservation
C – Community
D – Ecosystem
E – Biosphere
Match one of the definitions below to each term by writing down the number of the definition followed by the letter of the term that most accurately fits it.
(i)   A natural community of plants and animals.
(ii) The study of the interrelationships between living organisms and their environment.
(iii) The wise management and use of resources.
(iv) That part of the earth and its atmosphere inhabited by living things.
(v) A naturally occurring group of organisms inhabiting a common environment.

(b) The chart below shows the energy flow through a fresh-water eco-system

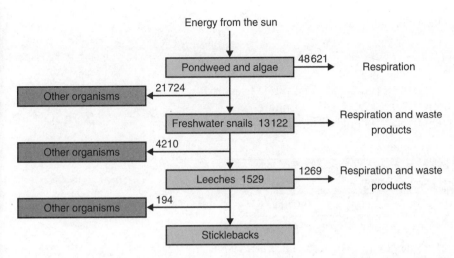

The units shown are in kilojoules per metre squared per year $(kJ\,m^{-2}\,year^{-1})$

(i)   Which organisms in this food chain are the primary consumers?

(ii) Calculate the gross primary production of the pondweed and algae.

(iii) How much energy is lost in respiration and waste products by the freshwater snails?

(iv) What is the percentage efficiency with which energy from leeches is passed down the food chain to the sticklebacks?

Answers to testing and applying knowledge on energetics

1. (a) A – petiole   B – lamina   C – cuticle
        D – epidermis   E – stomata   F – guard cells
        G – palisade mesophyll H – chloroplasts   I – thylakoids
        J – xylem   K – phloem

    (b) (i)   P – reduced nicotinamide adenine dinucleotide phosphate – $(NADPH + H^+)$ Q – starch
              R – carbon dioxide   S – glycerate-3-phosphate (GP)
         (ii) Five carbon atoms
         (iii) Glycerate-3-phosphate (GP)
         (iv) The triose sugar (which can be converted to glycerol) and glycerate-3-phosphate (which can be converted to fatty acids). Fatty acids + glycerol = fat.
         (v)   Oxygen (from photolysis of water).
         Reduced nicotinamide adenine dinucleotide phosphate $(NADPH + H^+)$; Adenosine triphosphate (ATP).

    (c) (i)   The relative amount of photosynthesis that takes place at different wavelengths of light.
         (ii) Blue light (400–450 nm with a peak at 430 nm); red light (600–700 nm with a peak at 660 nm).

      (iii)   Chlorophyll *a*   (blue-green);
                Chlorophyll *b*   (yellow-green);
                Xanthophyll   (yellow);
                Carotene   (yellow-orange).

2. (a) (i)   J – Iron   (ii)   G – Vitamin B_1 (thiamin)
        (iii)   D – Iodine   (iv)   F – Amino acids
        (v)   A – Calcium   (vi)   B – Vitamin D (calcified)
        (vii)   E – Vitamin C (ascorbic acid)   (viii)   I – Phosphate
        (ix)   B – Vitamin D (calciferol)   (x)   H – Lipid

    (b)

Name of enzyme	Source of enzyme	Substrate	Product(s)
(1) Maltase	Intestinal wall	Maltose	(2) Glucose
Rennin	(3) Stomach wall	(4) Caseinogen	(5) Casein
(6) Sucrase	(7) Intestinal wall	(8) Sucrose	Glucose and fructose
(9) Amylase	Salivary glands	(10) Amylose (starch)	(11) Maltose
Aminopeptidase	(12) Intestinal wall	(13) Peptides	(14) Amino acids
Chymotrypsin	(15) Pancreas	(16) Peptides	(17) Amino acids
(18) Lipase	(19) Pancreas	(20) Fats	Fatty acids and glycerol

3. (a) (i)   Glycolysis   (ii) Cytoplasm
        (iii)   Fructose bisphosphate   (iv) Phosphorylation

    (b) (i)   C = Pyruvate   (ii)   D = Ethanol
        (iii)   E = Lactate   (iv)   Fermentation

    (c) (i)   F = Acetyl coenzyme A   (ii)   G = Citrate
        (iii)   H = α-Ketoglutarate   (iv)   I = Oxaloacetate
        (v)   Krebs / Tricarboxylic acid (TCA) / Citric acid cycle
        (vi)   (cristae of) Mitochondria

    (d) (i)   Hydrogen ions
        (ii)   Nicotinamide adenine dinucleotide (NAD)
        (iii)   Oxygen
        (iv)   Cytochrome oxidase
        (v)   Cyanide

    (e) (i)   F   (ii) H   (iii) G
        (iv)   E   (v) F   (vi) C
        (vii)   Y

4. (a) (i)   D (Ecosystem)   (ii)   A (Ecology)   (iii)   B (Conservation)
        (iv)   E (Biosphere)   (v)   C (Community)

    (b) (i)   Freshwater snails
        (ii) $83\,467\ \text{kJ m}^{-2}\,\text{year}^{-1}$. Energy lost during respiration + energy consumed by snails and energy consumed by other organisms, i.e. $48\,621 + 13\,122 + 21\,724 = 83\,467$.
        (iii) $7383\ \text{kJ m}^{-2}\,\text{year}^{-1}$. Energy present in the snails less that consumed by leeches and other organisms, i.e.
        $13\,122 - (1529 + 4210) = 7383$.

(iv)   4.32%. You firstly need to calculate the energy passed down to the stickleback namely $1529 - (1269 + 194) = 66\,\mathrm{kJ\,m^{-2}\,year^{-1}}$. Then calculate the efficiency as follows: $66 \div 1529 \times 100 = 4.32\%$.

Sample question on energetics

(a)   The energy flow in a simple food web of five organisms A, B, C, D and E is shown below:

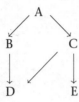

If organism C were suddenly removed from the food web describe, with reasons, the extent to which the populations of the other four organisms might be affected over time.   (*12 marks*)

(b)   The distribution of four species of organisms at different depths in a pond was investigated and the data presented graphically as shown below:

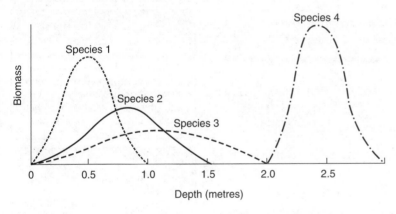

(i)   Giving your reasons, state which species is most likely to be the main primary producer.
(ii)   Which species is most likely to be a secondary consumer? Give reasons for your choice.   (*8 marks*)
(*Total 20 marks*)

Guided response to sample question on energetics

(a)   Given that the question states 'the extent to which the populations... might be affected over time', be sure to consider the **degree** of change **over a period**. As it is impossible to be certain precisely what might happen as we do not know the exact species involved, it is fair to assume that credit will be given for any reasonable response that can be supported by accepted ecological principles. In other words there may be no single correct answer.

Organisms A and B

The point here is that organism A is consumed by organism C and therefore:

√ the population of A will initially increase

√ due to a reduction in the number of its consumer – organism C.

However, organism B also feeds on organism A and therefore:

√ The increase in population A will mean a larger food supply is available for organism B whose population will probably increase as a result.

√ With a larger population of B consuming organism A, the latter's population will in turn decrease after a while

√ until a new equilibrium is established between the populations of A and B at which point both populations will stabilise

√ (BONUS) probably both at a level higher than the original because the total energy of the system is now shared between fewer species, some of which can therefore sustain a larger population.

This response assumes that these five organisms constitute the whole ecosystem, a highly unlikely situation but in the absence of other information this is the only way to view it.

Organism D

Organism D feeds on organism C (which has disappeared) and organism B (whose population has increased) therefore:

√ the population of D will initially decrease

√ because in the absence of organism C, its food supply is diminished

√ but as the population of B later increases so more food will be available to replace that lost as a result of organism C disappearing

√ and so the population of D will later recover.

√ The extent of this recovery depends on the degree to which the increase in the population of B can compensate for the loss of population C.

Organism E

Assuming there is no other food source than organism C on which organism E can live, then:

√ The population of E would decrease

√ ultimately becoming completely extinct.

√ The time scale for this extinction depends upon the internal and external food stores available to organism E.

(b) (i) The two important points to bear in mind when answering this question are the **depth** in the pond at which each species occurs and the **biomass** of each species. Remember that photosynthesis needs light and this is most available near to the surface of the pond, and rapidly diminishes the deeper one gets. Remember also that primary producers as a whole have greater biomass than all primary consumers. Considering these points your response to part (i) might be:

√ Species 1 is the primary producer

√ because primary producers are photosynthetic requiring light to make their food.

√ As light is more readily available at the surface of a pond they are more likely to be present in the upper levels of the pond and species 1 is found within the top metre with a maximum biomass at 0.5 m.

√ Furthermore species 1 has a large biomass (although not the largest), which is typical of primary producers.

(ii) In answer to this question you need also to consider the distribution of each species. Consumers, feeding as they do off another organism, must at some point, be found at the same depth as the species they feed upon – how else could they consume them if they were never in the same place? The curve for the secondary consumer

TUTORIAL TIP

Throughout your answer be sure to consider the **indirect**, as well as the **direct**, effects of the removal of organism C from the web.

TUTORIAL TIP

Always look to extend an argument/explanation to the full – making predictions as necessary. This can often earn valuable bonus marks.

TUTORIAL TIP

Further marks are not available for points already made so do not repeat here the reasons why population B has increased.

TUTORIAL TIP

Assume that the organisms shown represent the **whole** of the food web and do not attempt to consider the effects of other, hypothetical ones, which might also exist.

TUTORIAL TIP

It is the **area** under each curve that is a measure of total biomass not the maximum height of each curve.

TUTORIAL TIP

Use specific figures from the data provided to illustrate your points and so support your answer.

must therefore overlap with that of the primary consumer. This logic would appear to discount species 4, which does not occur at the same depth as any other besides which its biomass is the largest of those shown, making it highly unlikely to be a secondary consumer. Your answer might appear:

√ Species 3 is likely to be the secondary consumer

√ as it has the smallest biomass of the four species shown and,

√ since energy is lost at each stage in the food chain, so the biomass usually (but not always) reduces as one moves up the trophic levels.

√ Species 3 is found at the same depth as species 2 (their curves overlap), which is likely to be the primary consumer, as its biomass is intermediate between species 1 (producer) and species 3 (secondary consumer).

What then, you might ask, is species 4? Given its location at the lowest depth and its large biomass it is almost certainly a decomposer or detritivore. It feeds on dead and decaying remains that fall to the bottom – (hence its location) and it has a large biomass because it can feed on **all** the other species in the pond.

√ A well-argued elimination of species 4 might well earn a bonus mark.

Practice questions on energetics

Q. 1

The rate of carbon dioxide uptake in two species of plant was measured at different light intensities and the results were plotted on a graph.

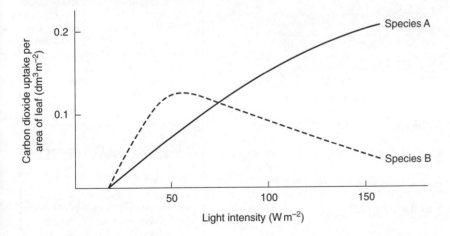

(a) (i) Which of the two species do you think is best adapted to shade conditions? *(1 mark)*

(ii) Give reasons for your answer *(2 marks)*

(b) Other than intensity, how else might light in a shaded area differ from that in a sunny one? *(1 mark)*

(c) Many species of plant that grow in shaded conditions have low rates of respiration. What is the possible advantage of this? *(2 marks)*

(d) Explain why it appears from the graph that there is no photosynthesis below a light intensity of $20\,W\,m^{-2}$ *(2 marks)*

TUTORIAL TIP

Carbon dioxide is a measure of the rate of photosynthesis. In part (a), consider which species is the most efficient at photosynthesising at low light intensities.

TUTORIAL TIP

Wherever possible support your answers with actual data from the graph.

(e) (i)   Which of the following would increase by four times the rate of
          photosynthesis of a plant in a laboratory where light was limiting
          photosynthesis?   (1 mark)
          1 – Increasing the carbon dioxide concentration four times.
          2 – Increasing the temperature by 20°C.
          3 – Increasing the temperature four times.
          4 – Halving the distance between the plant and the light source.
          5 – Reducing the distance between the plant and the light source to
          one-quarter of its original distance.
     (ii) Give reasons for your answer.   (2 marks)
                                                          (Total 11 marks)

Q. 2

The following table represents the results of an experiment in which the
stomach contents of 20 individuals were examined at regular intervals. In
each case the individuals were given 100 g of a particular food and by removing some of the stomach contents through a narrow tube, the length of time
the food remained in the stomach was ascertained. At the same time the
amount of acid present in the stomach was calculated by titration with a
suitable alkali.

Food eaten	Length of time food remained in stomach (minutes)	Amount of acid present (arbitrary units)
Bread	140	11
Rice (boiled)	130	12
Sugar (sucrose)	105	8
Cabbage	110	8
Apple	100	7
Chicken	200	15
Pork	200	15
Beef	175	16
Fish	160	15

> **TUTORIAL TIP**
>
> The words 'general type' in (a) (i) refer to a major category of food rather than a specific example such as 'chicken'.

> **TUTORIAL TIP**
>
> Notice the words 'than other types' in part (a) (ii). You should not only show why your chosen food remains longer in the stomach, but also why other foods do not.

> **TUTORIAL TIP**
>
> Your answer to (c) (i) is only expected to be an estimate and so a range of answers will be acceptable – but your response to (c) (ii) must be consistent with your estimate and be based on sound nutritional principles.

(a) (i)   Which general **type** of food remains in the stomach for the
          longest period of time?   (1 mark)
     (ii) Explain why this type of food should remain in the stomach
          longer than other types.   (3 marks)

(b) (i)   What correlation is there between the acid level and the length of
          time any particular food remains in the stomach?   (1 mark)
     (ii) Explain this correlation.   (4 marks)

(c) (i)   If the subject had been given green peas as one of the experimental
          foods, estimate the time it would have remained in the stomach and
          the acid level present.   (2 marks)
     (ii) Give reasons for your answer.   (3 marks)
                                                          (Total 14 marks)

Q. 3

(a) Give **one** example of (i) an endoparasite, (ii) an ectoparasite.(2 marks)

(b) Explain why parasites produce large numbers of offspring.   (3 marks)

(c) Differentiate between an obligate and facultative parasite. (2 marks)

(d) (i) List **three** ways in which parasites and saprophytes are similar.
(*3 marks*)

(ii) List **three** ways in which parasites and saprophytes differ.
(*3 marks*)

(e) State **four** advantages of saprophytes to man. (*4 marks*)
(*Total 17 marks*)

Q. 4

Two plant seedlings X and Y of different species had their respiratory quotients measured during their early development. The results are given in the table below:

No. of days from start of germination	X	Y
1	0.61	0.65
5	0.41	0.91
9	0.71	0.99
13	0.70	1.02

(a) What is meant by 'respiratory quotient'? (*1 mark*)

(b) Using the results of the experiment, discuss the possible nature of the respiratory substrates being used by X and Y. (*7 marks*)
(*Total 8 marks*)

Q. 5

Below is a diagram of a simple respirometer, which is used to measure the volume of oxygen taken up by organisms.

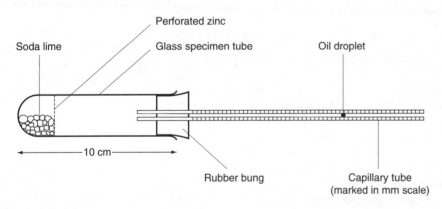

(a) (i) Suggest an organism that could be used in the apparatus. (*1 mark*)
(ii) Describe how the apparatus works and how you would use it.
(*10 marks*)

(iii) What control could be set up and how would it be used to modify the results obtained? (*4 marks*)

(b) List **four** sources of error that could arise when using the apparatus.
(*4 marks*)

(c) State **four** factors that could alter the rate of oxygen uptake by the organisms in the apparatus. (*4 marks*)

(d) If, during one experiment, the oil droplet moved 50 mm in 10 minutes and the total mass of the organisms in the glass specimen tube was 4 g, calculate the volume of oxygen taken up per hour, per gram of organism. NB: The capillary tube has a uniform bore of 1.0 mm. (*5 marks*)
(*Total 28 marks*)

TUTORIAL TIP

When listing differences between two things be sure to include the features of both, and not just state them for one, which leaves the reader to speculate on the other. A two column table is a useful way of presenting this sort of answer.

TUTORIAL TIP

You will need to know typical Respiratory Quotients for common storage products, e.g. carbohydrate = 1.0; lipid = 0.7; lipid conversion to carbohydrate = 0.35; protein = 0.8–0.9.

TUTORIAL TIP

Take note of the stated dimensions of the specimen tube before selecting a suitable organism to use.

TUTORIAL TIP

As the word 'volume' is used in the question it is necessary to explain in (a) (ii) **exactly** how this can be calculated.

Q. 6

What's lurking in the fridge?

Food poisoning in Britain has quadrupled in the past 10 years — there were more than 90 000 cases last year. Young children are particularly at risk of food poisoning and the number of cases increases in summer when warmer weather encourages the growth of bacteria.

Meat or poultry dishes are incriminated in about three-quarters of   5
cases of food poisoning that can be traced to a particular food. But food hygiene experts say that many cases could be prevented if meats were always eaten freshly cooked and hot. As convenience foods take over the supermarkets, tougher more virulent microbes are entering the food chain. One relative newcomer is VTEC — a member of the   10
Escherichia coli family of bacteria, which makes a powerful toxin that can cause kidney failure.

In 1994 an estimated quarter of million Americans got gastroenteritis by eating ice-cream — the largest outbreak of salmonella poisoning in the US ever traced to a single source. Environmental   15
health specialists eventually tracked down the cause. Liquid eggs laced with the bacteria *Salmonella* spp. were transported to a factory in tanker trailers. These same lorries later hauled pasteurised ice cream base to another plant, and the bacteria came too. Tiny amounts of *Salmonella* spp. ended up in the ice cream — only six   20
microscopic organisms per half cup (65 gram) serving — that was enough. But quality control procedures are often unable to detect such low levels of contamination.

The wise consumer practises defensive eating — treating most food as if it were packed with virulent bugs just waiting to gain access to   25
a warm, welcoming alimentary canal. Much of the time, you can't tell by look, smell or taste whether the food is contaminated. Sometimes food does smell or look 'off' but most infections are caught from food that seems perfectly normal.

Last year in Britain there were almost 50 000 reported cases of food   30
poisoning from the bacteria *Campylobacter* spp. — the most common cause — and numbers appear still to be rising each year. *Salmonella* was responsible for more than 30 000 reported cases. But these reported cases are just the tip of the iceberg. And there are a dozen or so other micro-organisms that can cause food poisoning too.   35

Both campylobacter and salmonella cause diarrhoea and abdominal pain; if you also vomit and run a high fever as well, the culprit is more likely to be salmonella. Salmonella usually makes itself felt somewhere between 12 and 48 hours after eating the contaminated meal, but campylobacter can strike up to 10 days later, although   40
between 2 and 5 days' delay is more common.

Both bacteria are common in raw poultry. Poisoning usually stems from eating undercooked chicken. But you can get the bug from eating any food that has come into contact with raw poultry. A *Which?* survey in 1994 found that 36 per cent of raw chickens on   45
sale contained salmonella while 41 per cent contained campylobacter. But these microbes also lurk in meat, milk and even household pets — environmental health officers recently traced a case of salmonella poisoning to a family's pet iguana.

You don't have to go travelling in a developing country to catch   50
dysentery (Latin: 'bad bowels') from contaminated food. In Britain it is on the increase. An outbreak in southern England in 1994 caused by *Shigella sonnei* was traced to imported iceberg lettuces. Viral

hepatitis (hepatitis A), a severe liver infection, is classically
linked to contaminated shellfish.   55
    Even vegans, who fare so well in most food scares, do not escape the
risk of food poisoning altogether. Cereal products, spices and especially cornflour sauce and cooked rice and pasta dishes can provide
a home to *Bacillus cereus*, which causes nausea, vomiting, stomach
cramps and sometimes diarrhoea.   60

> From an article by Gail Vines – *The Guardian* on 25 June 1996.

Using information from the article and your own knowledge answer the
following questions:

(a)   What is meant by the following terms:
      (i)   'toxin' (line 11)   (*1 mark*)
      (ii)   'pasteurised' (line 18)   (*1 mark*)
      (iii) 'virulent' (line 25)   (*1 mark*)

(b)   (i)   Explain why 'Young children are particularly at risk of food
      poisoning' (lines 2–4)   (*2 marks*)
      (ii)   Apart from 'encouraging the growth of bacteria' why else might
      'the number of cases [of food poisoning] increase in the summer'?
      (line 4)   (*3 marks*)

(c)   (i)   What percentage of reported cases of food poisoning in 1995 were
      the result of *Salmonella*?   (*1 mark*)
      (ii)   How many cases of food poisoning were there in 1985? (*1 mark*)

(d)   What precautions might you take at home in order to avoid food
poisoning?   (*6 marks*)

(e)   What might you do if you suspect that you have contracted food
poisoning from a food source some of which is still left?   (*4 marks*)

(f)   Give **one disadvantage** of each of the following actions upon sus-
pecting you have food poisoning:
      (i)   taking antibiotics;   (*1 mark*)
      (ii)   taking anti-diarrhoea medicines.   (*1 mark*)
                                                          (*Total 22 marks*)

Answers to practice questions on energetics

1.   (a)   (i)   √ Species B
               (ii)   √ The uptake of carbon dioxide is a measure of the rate of
               photosynthesis
               √   At low light intensities (10–80 W m^{-2}) i.e. shaded conditions,
               species B has a higher rate of photosynthesis than species A, which
               photosynthesises best at higher light intensities (100–150 W m^{-2}).

         (b)   √   The light is likely to be of a longer wavelength because it will
         have been reflected from/filtered through other vegetation, which will
         absorb the shorter wavelengths.

         (c)   √   In the shade, photosynthesis is less because it is limited
         by low light intensity and so plants in these conditions produce less
         carbohydrate and oxygen – both the raw materials of respiration.
         √   By reducing their respiration rate, shade plants retain more
         valuable carbohydrate so that sufficient is retained to synthesise into
         other materials, such as protein for growth.

(d) $\checkmark$ The rate of photosynthesis in this experiment is measured as uptake of carbon dioxide. Some photosynthesis **does** take place below $20\,W\,m^{-2}$, but the carbon dioxide needed for this comes from that produced during respiration, rather than by absorption from outside.

$\checkmark$ Above light intensities of $20\,W\,m^{-2}$ the rate of carbon dioxide uptake by photosynthesis exceeds that produced by respiration and so a net uptake of carbon dioxide occurs.

(e) (i) $\checkmark$ Number 4.

(ii) $\checkmark$ As light is the limiting factor in this case, only an increase in the amount of light can increase the rate of photosynthesis. This leaves only options 4 and 5. The light intensity is inversely proportional to the square of the distance from the source.

$\checkmark$ Halving the distance therefore increases the rate of photosynthesis by $2^2 = 4$ times (In option 5 it would increase the rate by $2^4 = 16$ times).

2.   (a) (i) $\checkmark$ Protein

(ii) $\checkmark$ Protein is digested in the stomach by the enzyme pepsin, which works best at a pH of around 2 or 3 – conditions maintained by the secretion of hydrochloric acid.

$\checkmark$ Protein therefore remains a long time in the stomach as conditions here allow its efficient breakdown, whereas elsewhere in the intestine a lack of pepsin and a higher pH would inhibit its digestion.

$\checkmark$ The low pH and lack of non-protein digesting enzymes means that little, if any, digestion of other foods can take place in the stomach and these therefore pass through quickly.

(b) (i) $\checkmark$ The greater the acid level the longer the food remains in the stomach.

(ii) $\checkmark$ Hydrochloric acid is essential to protein digestion because it converts inactive pepsinogen into active pepsin / provides the optimum pH for the pepsin to breakdown protein.

$\checkmark$ The presence of food stimulates the stomach lining to produce the hormone gastrin.

$\checkmark$ Gastrin circulates in the blood and causes the oxyntic cells of the stomach to produce hydrochloric acid, and so,

$\checkmark$ the longer that food is present in the stomach the longer hydrochloric acid is produced and the greater will be the acid level.

(c) (i) $\checkmark$ 125 minutes (range approx. 115–130).

$\checkmark$ 10 units of acid (range approx. 9–11).

(ii) $\checkmark$ In general the length of time food remains in the stomach and hence the acid level is related to the protein content of the food.

$\checkmark$ Peas have a protein content a little below that of rice, but much higher than that of cabbage. (Typical values: rice 6.2%, peas 5.0%, cabbage 1.7% although you would not be expected to know precise values.)

$\checkmark$ The estimates are therefore based on values between those for rice and cabbage but nearer those for rice than those for cabbage.

3. (a) √√ Any suitable example will gain credit. Some possible responses are:

   (i) *Plasmodium* (malarial parasite); *Fasciola* (liver fluke); *Taenia* (tapeworm).

   (ii) *Pulex* (flea); *Argas* (tick); *Sarcoptes* (mite).

(b) √ Most parasites can only survive on a specific host and individual hosts do not live forever – and so parasites need to find new ones.

√ New hosts are not always readily available, easy to find or easily invaded, and so many offspring are needed to increase the possibility of at least one succeeding in finding a new host.

√ Many offspring need to spend a period outside of their host and this leads to a large loss of individuals. A large number of offspring are needed to compensate for this.

(c) √ Obligate parasites **have** to live parasitically because they cannot obtain their nutrition in any other way.

√ Facultative parasites **usually** live parasitically but may continue to feed on their dead host by saprophytic means.

(d) (i) √√√ Any one from the following list to a maximum of three:

   • nutrition is heterotrophic;
   • simple food substances are absorbed;
   • digestive systems are simple or absent altogether;
   • produce large numbers of offspring;
   • reproduction entails sexual and asexual stages;
   • resistant stages are often a feature of the life cycle.

   (ii) √√√ Any one comparison from the following table to a maximum of three:

Parasites	Saprophytes
Energy is derived from living organisms	Energy is derived from dead organisms
Have very restricted nutritional requirements often living off a single species	Use a wide variety of food sources
Have very specialised and highly adapted means of obtaining their food	Use simple methods to obtain their food
Mostly aerobic respiration is used	Aerobic and anaerobic respiration is common
The life cycle often has many stages	There are often fewer stages in the life cycle
Most plant and animal groups have parasitic representatives.	Almost totally limited to the Prokaryotae and Fungi

(e) √√√√ Any from the following list to a maximum of four:
• recycle nutrients such as carbon and nitrogen and so maintain atmospheric composition and soil fertility;
• source of food e.g. mushrooms;
• baking bread and brewing wines and beers using yeasts;
• manufacture of foods e.g. cheese, yoghurt;
• production of antibiotics e.g. penicillin;
• decomposition of sewage;
• important in certain industrial/biotechnological processes, e.g. production of hormones, vitamins, enzymes, fuels.

4.   (a)   √ Respiratory quotient (RQ) is the ratio of the volume of carbon dioxide expired to the volume of oxygen consumed over a given period.

     (b)   **Species X**

√   In the early stages the RQ of 0.61 is probably due to the complete metabolism of lipid to carbon dioxide and water (RQ = 0.7) and

√   a little conversion of lipid to carbohydrate (RQ = 0.35).

√   The proportion of lipid conversion to carbohydrate increases (RQ = 0.41 after 5 days)

√   Thereafter lipid alone is being respired (RQ = 0.7)

√   (ALTERNATIVE) lipid is still being converted to carbohydrate (RQ = 0.35) and the carbohydrate is then being respired (RQ = 1.0). The balance between these two processes leads to a RQ of 0.71/0.70.

Species Y

√   Initially lipid is being respired (RQ = 0.7) with perhaps a little being converted to carbohydrate (RQ = 0.35).

√   Thereafter the amount of lipid respired is reduced and the amount of carbohydrate (either stored or made from lipid) respired is increased and

√   there is hence a gradual increase in RQ from 0.91 to 1.0, until on day 13 only carbohydrate is being respired. (NB: Because protein is essential for growth it is rarely used as a respiratory substitute by seeds.)

5.   (a)   (i)   √ Any organism that is large enough to handle but small enough to be contained within the tube, e.g. woodlouse, maggot, locust, beetle, horsefly, earthworm, germinating peas.

         (ii)   √ An individual or group of organisms to be used should be weighed and placed in the specimen tube.

√   The oil droplet should be positioned about half-way along the tube so that when the bung is inserted the droplet is forced to the end furthest from the specimen tube.

√   The position of the droplet should be recorded and timing commenced.

√   The organism(s) respire(s) according to the equation

$$C_6H_{12}O_6 + 6O_2 \rightarrow 6CO_2 + 6H_2O + \text{Energy}$$

√   The carbon dioxide produced is absorbed by the soda-lime reducing it to a negligible volume.

√   Any water vapour produced will also be absorbed by the soda-lime so that its volume too can be ignored.

√   The only measurable volume change is therefore due to the intake of oxygen by the organism(s).

√   This reduction in volume leads to a reduction in pressure within the apparatus.

√   Atmospheric pressure now exceeds the pressure inside the apparatus and so the droplet is pushed towards the specimen tube.

√   The time taken for the droplet to move a set distance is recorded and the process repeated a number of times to allow an average to be calculated.

√   The actual volume is calculated using the formula for the volume of a cylinder, namely $\pi r^2 h$. where 'h' is the average distance moved by the droplet and 'r' is the radius of the capillary tube.

√   The radius of the capillary tube can be determined by finding its internal diameter using a travelling microscope and then halving the value.

$\sqrt{}$ The average volume of oxygen consumed should be divided by the average duration of the trials and then by the weight of the organism(s) to give a value of oxygen consumed $min^{-1} g^{-1}$.

(Maximum marks = 10)

(iii) $\sqrt{}$ Use a second set of apparatus but exclude the organism(s).
$\sqrt{}$ All other conditions should be identical as far as possible and the two experiments should be run simultaneously.
$\sqrt{}$ If there is a movement of the droplet in the control apparatus an adjustment should be made to the experimental reading.
$\sqrt{}$ For example if the control droplet moves away from the specimen tube the distance moved should be added to the value in the experimental tube – if it moves towards the specimen tube it should be subtracted.

(b) $\sqrt{}\sqrt{}\sqrt{}\sqrt{}$ Any from the following list to a maximum of four:
• apparatus not air tight;
• temperature changes during the experiment (will alter pressure);
• pressure changes during the experiment;
• soda lime may be exhausted (i.e. has ceased to absorb more carbon dioxide);
• capillary tube may not be horizontal (gravity may move droplet);

(c) $\sqrt{}\sqrt{}\sqrt{}\sqrt{}$ Any four of the following five points:
• external temperature fluctuations;
• age of the organisms;
• activity of the organisms (i.e. stationary or moving);
• amount of oxygen available in the specimen tube;
• light intensity (may affect activity of the animals or photosynthesis in plants).

(d) $\sqrt{}$ The movement of the droplet means that the organism(s) have absorbed a cylinder of oxygen some 50 mm long.
$\sqrt{}$ The formula for the volume of a cylinder is $\pi r^2 h$. In this case:
$$h = 50\,mm$$

$$r = \frac{1.0}{2} = 0.5\,mm$$

Therefore volume $= \pi \times (0.5)^2 \times 50$.
$\sqrt{}$ To calculate volume of oxygen consumed in 1 hour we need to multiply by 6 ($6 \times 10\,min = 1$ hour)
$\sqrt{}$ To calculate the oxygen consumed per gram we need to divide by 4 (total weight = 4 g).
$\sqrt{}$ The value is therefore:

$$\frac{\pi \times (0.5)^2 \times 50 \times 6}{4} = 58.9\,mm^3\,hr^{-1}\,g^{-1}$$

6.   (a) (i) $\sqrt{}$ A poisonous organic substance.
(ii) $\sqrt{}$ Heat treatment for food (usually milk) to extend its shelf-life by reducing its microbial content. The milk is either heated to around 65°C for 30 minutes or to 71.5°C for 15 seconds.
(iii) $\sqrt{}$ Highly poisonous / able to cause disease.

(b) (i)   √ Young children have often not yet acquired immunity to particular diseases. Their first exposure to any infection is therefore often much more severe than subsequent ones.

√   They may not yet have been taught or understand the importance of basic hygiene (washing of hands after using the toilet / before eating). Even where they have, they may forget to follow guidelines!

(ii)   √ There are more picnics / outdoor eating where food is not eaten hot and immediately after it has been prepared – such foods are more prone to carrying infection.

√   Food eaten outdoors is more exposed to contamination by flies and other insects, which can carry infection.

√   Barbecues are common in warm weather and the food may not be thoroughly cooked because there is rarely accurate timing or temperature control – much is guesswork. Undercooking food, especially meat, does not destroy all the microorganisms it contains.

(c) (i)   √ 60% (30 000 *Salmonella* cases out of a total of 50 000 cases – lines 30 and 33).

(ii)   √ 22 500 (90 000 cases 'last year' 1995 and the 'numbers have quadrupled in 10 years' – lines 1–2).

(d) Any six from the following examples:

√   Thoroughly cook all eggs, poultry and other meat – especially if cooked from frozen.

√   Defrost food completely before cooking unless instructions say it can be cooked from frozen.

√   Be sure that reheated food / leftovers are very hot throughout.

√   Cool leftovers immediately and store them at as low a temperature as possible.

√   Store raw and cooked foods separately – if this is impractical then keep raw foods at the bottom of the fridge and cooked ones at the top.

√   Use separate utensils for raw and cooked food.

√   Eat foods by their 'use by' date.

√   Keep work surfaces and cooking / storage utensils clean.

√   Keep pets / insects / vermin away from food preparation areas.

√   Abide by basic hygiene guidelines e.g. wash hands before handling food.

(e) √   Inform your doctor.

√   Inform all others who may have eaten the same food, or been contaminated by you.

√   Keep the suspect food in a sealed container in the fridge as it may need to be tested for infection.

√   Drink plenty of water with a little sugar and salt to avoid dehydration from diarrhoea.

(f) (i)   √ Taking antibiotics can lead to the build up of resistance in the disease-causing agent, rendering it ineffective in future cases. This use is therefore normally restricted to vulnerable groups such as the young, elderly and infirm.

(ii)   √ Diarrhoea is the body's mechanism for rapidly removing the disease causing agent. Anti-diarrhoea medicines may therefore result in the infection remaining in the body longer, allowing its toxins to cause more harm.

6 TRANSPORT AND EXCHANGE MECHANISMS

Breathing and gaseous exchange in mammals

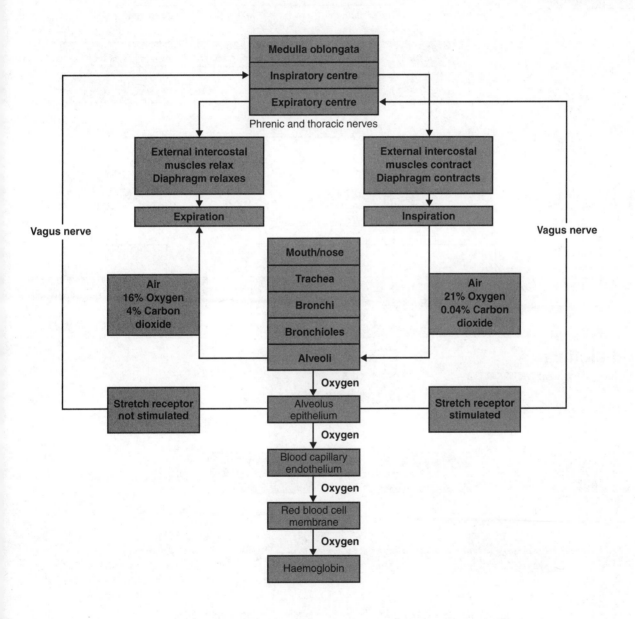

Components of human blood

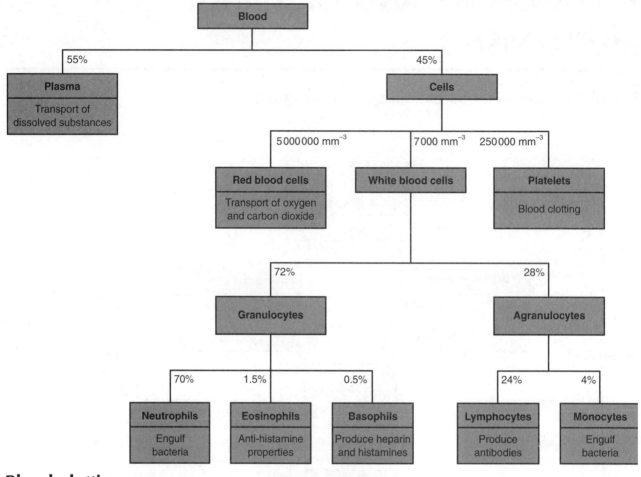

Blood clotting

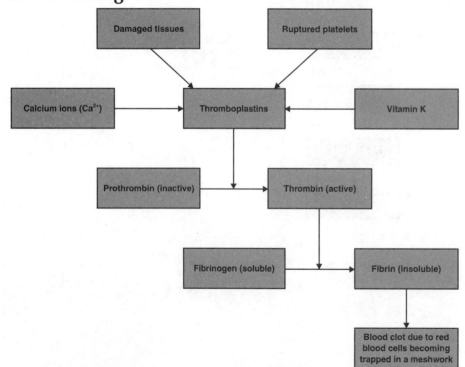

Mammalian circulatory system

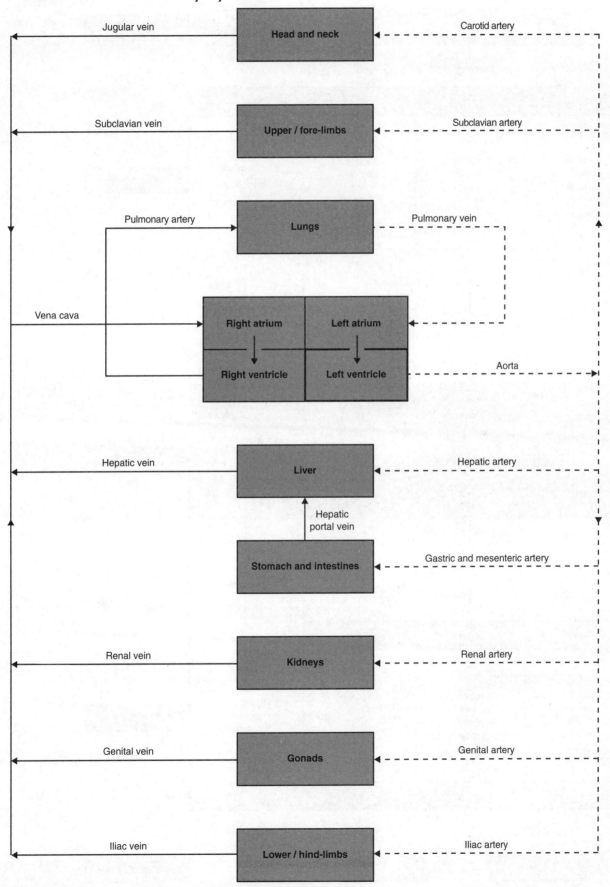

Uptake and transport in plants

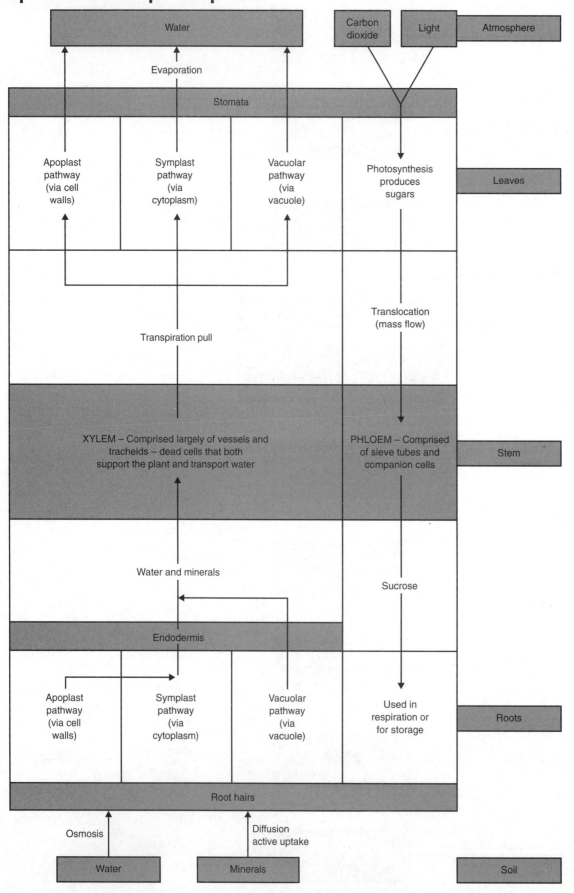

Osmoregulation and excretion in the mammalian kidney

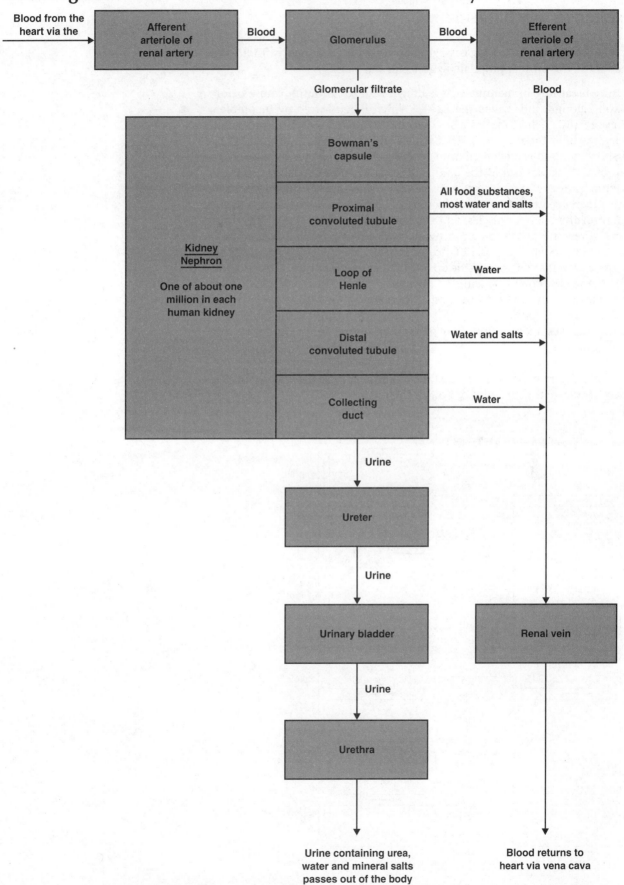

Testing and applying knowledge on transport exchange mechanisms

1. Complete the following passage about gaseous exchange by finding for each letter the most appropriate word to fill the blank.

During breathing in mammals air is drawn into the mouth or nose before passing along a tube called the ...(A)... which is reinforced by incomplete rings of ...(B).... This tube branches to form two ...(C)... which in turn subdivide into finer tubes called ...(D)... which end in air-sacs or alveoli. When swallowing, food is prevented from entering the oesophagus by means of a flap of cartilage known as the ...(E).... If air is to enter the lungs, from the exterior, pressure inside them must be ...(F)... than that of the atmosphere. This is achieved by the rib cage moving upwards and outwards due to the action of the ...(G)... muscles, and the flattening of the ...(H).... Breathing out is a reversal of the same process with air leaving by the same route – an air-flow described as ...(I).... Once air is in the alveoli, oxygen will diffuse across their walls which are made up of ...(J)... epithelium into red blood cells where it readily combines with the pigment ...(K).... The oxygenated blood then passes to the heart via the ...(L)... [two words]. Breathing is controlled by a respiratory centre in the ...(M)... [two words] region of the brain. This centre receives information from stretch receptors in the lung via the ...(N)... nerve.

2. The diagram below is a plan of the mammalian circulatory system. The arrows indicate the direction of flow of the blood.

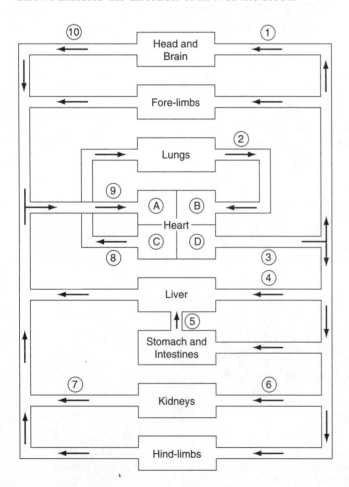

(a)   Give the names of the vessels numbered 1–10.

(b)   List **four** differences between the composition of blood in vessel 6 and its composition in vessel 7.

(c)   (i)   Name the chambers of the heart labelled A and D.
      (ii)   Which letter depicts the chamber with the thickest wall?
      (iii) Name the valves found between chambers B and D.
      (iv)   Name the valves found in vessel 3.

(d)   List **two** differences between the circulatory system shown and that of a fish.

3.   When a sample of blood from each of five humans was tested with blood typing sera anti-A, anti-B and anti-D (rhesus) the following results were obtained:

	anti-A	anti-B	anti-D
Human 1	no change	agglutination	agglutination
Human 2	no change	no change	no change
Human 3	agglutination	no change	no change
Human 4	agglutination	agglutination	agglutination
Human 5	agglutination	agglutination	no change

(a)   Which individuals are rhesus negative?

(b)   Which individual has blood whose only antigen is A?

(c)   State the individuals with the following blood groups:
      (i) AB positive; (ii) O negative; (iii) B positive.

(d)   Which individual is termed the 'universal donor'?

4.   The diagrams below are transverse sections through the stem and root of a flowering plant and show the distribution of the various tissues.

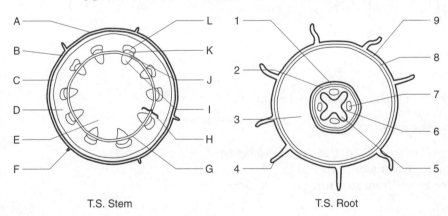

T.S. Stem   T.S. Root

(a)   Indicate by means of the appropriate letter on the diagram of the stem, the labelled part which best fits each of the following descriptions. Each letter may be used once, more than once, or not at all:
      (i)   The region known as the pith.
      (ii)   Sclerenchyma.
      (iii) The tissue that transports water up the plant.
      (iv)   The tissue that transports sugars.
      (v)   A single-celled layer.

(vi) Tissue made up largely of fibres.
(vii) Made up largely of cutin.
(viii) Made up in part of sieve tube elements.
(ix) The tissue whose contents are normally under tension.
(x)   Living cells with additional thickening of cellulose in parts of their cell wall.

(b) (i) Label the parts numbered 1–9 on the diagram of the root.
(ii) State **two** abiotic factors affecting water absorption by the roots.
(iii) State **two** functions other than absorption, performed by at least some roots.

5. The diagram below illustrates a nephron from a mammalian kidney.

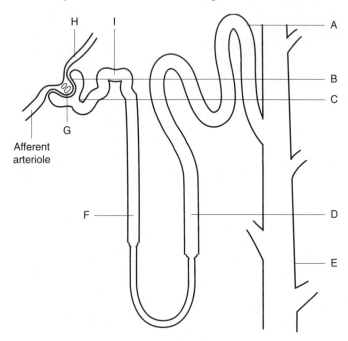

(a) Name the parts labelled A–I.

(b) (i) Name a substance found in the fluid in the afferent arteriole but **not** present in the structure labelled I.
(ii) Why is this substance absent from structure I?

(c) (i) Name a substance found in the fluid in the structure labelled I, but absent from the fluid in the structure labelled D.
(ii) Why is this substance absent from structure D?

(d) Give the letter of the structure which:
(i)   has the highest concentration of urea;
(ii) is made up of podocytes;
(iii) has its permeability affected by anti-diuretic hormone (ADH) – two answers;
(iv) helps to control blood pH;
(v)   possesses microvilli.

Answers to testing and applying knowledge on transport and exchange mechanisms

1. A = trachea   B = cartilage   C = bronchi
    D = bronchioles   E = epiglottis   F = lower
    G = (external)intercostal H = diaphragm   I = tidal
    J = squamous   K = haemoglobin   L = pulmonary vein
    M = medulla oblongata   N = vagus

2. (a) 1 = carotid artery   2 = pulmonary vein   3 = aorta
         4 = hepatic artery   5 = hepatic portal vein 6 = renal artery
         7 = renal vein   8 = pulmonary artery   9 = vena cava
         10 = jugular vein

    (b) Vessel 6   Vessel 7
         more oxygen   less oxygen
         less carbon dioxide   more carbon dioxide
         more glucose   less glucose
         more urea   less urea
         (more water)*   (less water)*
         (more salts)*   (less salts)*
    *Normally the case, but the relative amounts of these are very variable.

    (c) (i)   A = right atrium; D = left ventricle
         (ii)   Chamber D
         (iii) Bicuspid (mitral) valves
         (iv)   Semi-lunar valves

    (d) Any two from:
         Mammal   Fish
         Double circulation   Single circulation
         Four-chambered heart   Two-chambered heart
         No sinus venosus   Sinus venosus present adjacent to the
                                 atrium
         No renal portal system Renal portal system

3. (a) Individuals 2, 3 and 5 (no agglutination with serum anti-D).

    (b) Individual 3 (agglutination only occurs with serum anti-A).

    (c) (i)   Individual 4 (agglutination with all three sera).
         (ii)   Individual 2 (agglutination with no sera).
         (iii) Individual 1 (agglutination with anti-B and anti-D).

    (d) Individual 2 (no agglutination with any sera and therefore has no
    antigens to react with recipient's antibodies).

4. (a) (i) E; (ii) L; (iii) I; (iv) K; (v) B; (vi) L; (vii) A; (viii) K; (ix) I; (x) C.

    (b) (i)   1 = endodermis   2 = pericycle
                3 = cortex of parenchyma 4 = root hair
                5 = xylem   6 = cambium
                7 = phloem   8 = exodermis
                9 = piliferous (epidermal) layer
         (ii)   Temperature and the osmotic potential of the soil solution.
         (iii) Choose any two from:
                Storage of food material
                Anchorage of the plant
                Asexual reproduction (vegetative propagation).

5. (a) A = Distal convoluted (coiled) tubule.
         B = Visceral wall of Bowman's capsule.
         C = Parietal wall of Bowman's capsule.
         D = Ascending limb of loop of Henle.
         E = Collecting duct.
         F = Descending limb of loop of Henle.
         G = Glomerular capillary (glomerulus).
         H = Efferent arteriole
         I = Proximal convoluted (coiled) tubule.

   (b) (i)   Protein molecules
       (ii) The pressure created by ultra-filtration in the glomerulus (G)
       is only sufficient to squeeze out the blood molecules up to a
       relative molecular mass (RMM) of 68 000. Protein molecules
       have a greater RMM.

   (c) (i) Any organic food substance, e.g. glucose, amino acids.
       (ii) Food substances are completely reabsorbed in the proximal
       convoluted tubule (I).

   (d) (i) E; (ii) B; (iii) A and E; (iv) A; (v) I.

Sample question on transport and exchange mechanisms

In an experiment conducted at 20°C, young maize seedlings had their roots
placed in distilled water for 12 hours. Samples of equal mass were then taken
periodically and the amount of potassium they contained was estimated.
After 45 minutes the seedlings left were transferred from distilled water to
a 0.1-M solution of potassium chloride and equal mass samples were again
taken and estimated for their potassium content. Two hours later some
potassium cyanide solution was added to the remaining seedlings before
they in turn were sampled. The experiment was then repeated at 0°C. The
results are displayed graphically below:

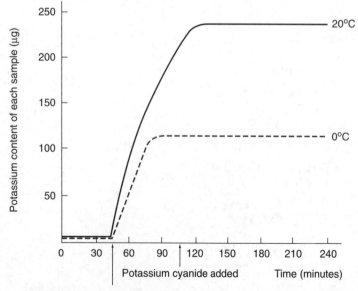

Transfer from distilled water to
0.1 M potassium chloride solution

(a) (i)   the similarities between the two lines;   (*3 marks*)
     (ii) the main difference between the two lines.   (*1 mark*)

(b) Explain why the uptake of potassium ions is greater at 20°C than at 0°C.   (*5 marks*)

(c) With reference to the curves for both temperatures, explain the effect of adding potassium cyanide.   (*5 marks*)

(d) After 240 minutes the maize seedlings that had been kept at 25°C were washed in distilled water and approximately 20% of the total potassium content was extracted by this means. What does this indicate about the location of:
     (i)   the potassium that was not extracted and
     (ii) the potassium that was washed out?   (*4 marks*)
                                              (*Total 18 marks*)

Guided response to sample question on transport and exchange mechanisms

(a) (i)   In comparing the two lines, consider them in relation to the three phases of the experiment:
- when growing in distilled water (0–45 min);
- after the addition of potassium chloride but prior to adding potassium cyanide (45–105 min);
- after the addition of potassium cyanide (105–240 min).

We can then see that there is one similarity in each phase, namely:

√ there is no uptake of potassium ions initially / when grown in distilled water / up to 45 min;

√ there is a very rapid uptake of potassium ions in the first 25 minutes after the addition of potassium chloride;

√ ultimately no further potassium ions are absorbed.

(ii) The main difference occurs during the middle phase:

√ between 75 and 120 minutes the uptake of potassium ions at 20°C continues whereas it ceases at 0°C.

(b) In answering part (b), begin by considering the mechanisms by which potassium ions are absorbed by plant roots and then look at how temperature might affect each of these.

√ Potassium ions can be absorbed by diffusion, a passive process, in roots via the root hairs.

√ Higher temperatures increase the kinetic energy of potassium ions, which therefore move across the cell membrane of the root hairs more quickly at 20°C than 0°C.

√ Potassium ions can also be taken up by active means – a process requiring energy.

√ The necessary energy is released during respiration.

√ The higher the temperature, the greater the rate of respiration, the faster the energy is released, and so the faster the rate of uptake of potassium ions by active means.

√ (BONUS) For any **quantitative** data to support your arguments, e.g. the rate of diffusion / respiration approximately doubles for a 10°C rise in temperature. Alternatively some reference to actual figures from the graph.

TUTORIAL TIP

Do not be **too** eager to get on with your answer to this question. It is important to fully appreciate what exactly is happening in the experiment, so take time to read the details carefully and only proceed once you feel you understand them.

TUTORIAL TIP

Both the word 'explain' in the question and the allocation of five marks to this part of the question indicate that **detail** is needed. It is not sufficient to say 'diffusion is faster at higher temperatures' but rather an explanation in terms of kinetic theory is necessary.

(c)   The essential point here is that cyanide inhibits cellular respiration and so prevents the release of energy. The active uptake of potassium ions will therefore be affected, but **not** their uptake by diffusion.

√ Cyanide compounds prevent cellular respiration

√ by inhibiting the enzyme cytochrome oxidase that catalyses the transfer of hydrogen atoms from the cytochromes of the electron transport system to oxygen molecules.

√ ATP is therefore no longer produced, preventing active absorption and so the rate of uptake of potassium ions no longer increases, at 25°C.

√ There is no effect on the rate of absorption at 0°C since at this temperature there is little or no cellular respiration, and hence ATP production is negligible.

√ Some absorption still takes place at both temperatures due to diffusion – a process that does not require ATP/energy and so is not affected by the presence of cyanide.

(d)   The differentially permeable nature of the cell membrane is the relevant factor here. It has the ability to prevent the entry and escape of substances as necessary and so chemicals that would otherwise diffuse out along a concentration gradient can be retained. Equally the role of the casparian strip of the endodermis is as important as it too acts as a block to diffusion. Your response might therefore be:

(i)   √ The potassium that is not extracted is either that **within cells,** which is retained because the cell membrane prevents its outward diffusion,

√ or that which has already moved beyond the endodermis and diffusion is therefore blocked by the endodermis.

(ii)   √ The potassium washed out was situated outside cells and therefore freely diffused out along a concentration gradient;

√ e.g. it was in the cell walls and/or the intercellular spaces of the root cortex.

> ### TUTORIAL TIP
>
> Remember to explain why there is still some potassium uptake despite there being no energy available from respiration.

Practice questions on transport and exchange mechanisms

Q. 1
The lung volume of an adult human was measured by a spirometer during a variety of breathing exercises and the following traces obtained:

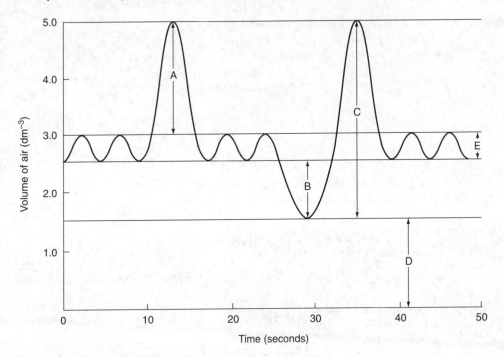

(a) By means of an appropriate letter state which volume represents:
    (i)   inspiratory reserve volume;   *(1 mark)*
    (ii) expiratory reserve volume;   *(1 mark)*
    (iii) tidal volume;   *(1 mark)*
    (iv) residual volume;   *(1 mark)*
    (v) vital capacity.   *(1 mark)*

(b) In another experiment a subject was given various gaseous mixtures to breathe and the rate of breathing measured. The results are shown below:

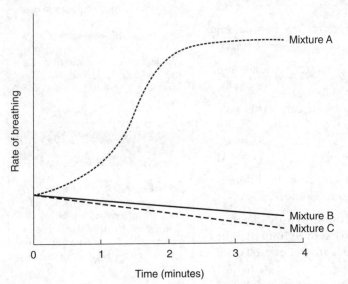

TUTORIAL TIP

To answer part (b) you will need to know the relative concentration of carbon dioxide and oxygen in normal atmospheric air.

Mixture A = 90% oxygen + 10% carbon dioxide
Mixture B = normal atmospheric air
Mixture C = 100% oxygen

(i) Explain what the data show concerning how the rate of breathing is controlled. *(2 marks)*

(ii) In the light of the information provided by the graph show why mouth-to-mouth resuscitation is a better means of artificial respiration than pressing on the chest wall. *(3 marks)*

(c) Explain fully why it is more dangerous to re-breathe expired air if it is first passed through soda-lime. *(5 marks)*

(d) An athlete has a maximum air intake of $20\,dm^3\,min^{-1}$. She can incur an oxygen debt of $14\,dm^3$ before she collapses. Running at $5\,m\,sec^{-1}$ she uses oxygen at a rate of $0.3\,dm^3\,sec^{-1}$. How far can she run before collapsing?

(4 marks)

(Total 19 marks)

TUTORIAL TIP

It is essential to show all your working in part (d). There may be as little as one mark for the correct answer with the remainder being credited for the method of working. It follows that a wrong calculation based on an accurate method can still gain the majority of the marks.

Q. 2

The percentage saturation of adult human haemoglobin with oxygen was measured at two different partial pressures of carbon dioxide. The results are presented in the table below:

Partial pressure of oxygen (kPa)	% saturation of haemoglobin with oxygen	
	CO_2 partial pressure = 2 kPa	CO_2 partial pressure = 10 kPa
1	9	2
2	23	10
3	39	21
4	56	35
5	70	50
6	79	62
8	89	75
10	95	85
12	98	92

(a) Using these data, plot oxygen dissociation curves for the two partial pressures of carbon dioxide. *(4 marks)*

(b) Describe the effect of increasing carbon dioxide pressure on the oxygen carrying capacity of haemoglobin. *(2 marks)*

(c) Where in the human body is the partial pressure of carbon dioxide likely to be:

(i) high *(1 mark)*

(ii) low *(1 mark)*

(d) How does this variation in carbon dioxide concentration in different regions of the body affect the transport of oxygen by the blood? *(2 marks)*

(e) For each of the following types of haemoglobin or respiratory pigment state whether the oxygen dissociation curve lies to the left or right of that for adult human haemoglobin and give one reason for your answer in each case:

(i) human myoglobin; *(2 marks)*

(ii) human foetal haemoglobin; *(2 marks)*

TUTORIAL TIP

As always when plotting graphs choose axes carefully with the independent variable on the x-axis (abscissa/horizontal) and the dependent variable on the y-axis (ordinate/vertical). Label the axes with the appropriate scale, state the variable being measured with units and distinguish by labelling the two.

TUTORIAL TIP

Remember that respiratory pigments with curves to the left of adult human haemoglobin have a greater affinity for oxygen and therefore pick it up more readily but release it less easily. The opposite is true of curves to the right.

TUTORIAL TIP

In answering part (e) bear in mind that a respiratory pigment's affinity for oxygen will need to be greater where the availability of oxygen is low and/or the demand for it by the organism is high.

(iii) mouse haemoglobin;   *(2 marks)*
(iv) llama haemoglobin;   *(2 marks)*
(v) pigeon haemoglobin.   *(2 marks)*
                                                             (Total 20 marks)

Q. 3

The diagram below shows a vertical section through the human heart as viewed from the front. Labels A–D are the chambers of the heart, M and N major blood vessels and X, Y and Z structures concerned with the control of the heart beat.

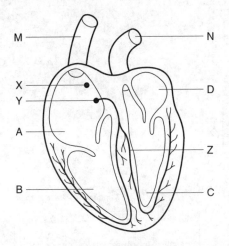

(a) Using the appropriate letter, state which chamber of the heart:
(i) is the left atrium;
(ii) pumps deoxygenated blood to the lungs;
(iii) would be first to receive amino acids absorbed from the ileum.
                                                             (3 marks)

(b) (i) Name each of the structures X, Y and Z, which control heartbeat.
                                                             (3 marks)
(ii) Outline the functions of each of X, Y and Z   *(3 marks)*

(c) The graph below charts pressure changes in the left atrium, left ventricle and aorta.

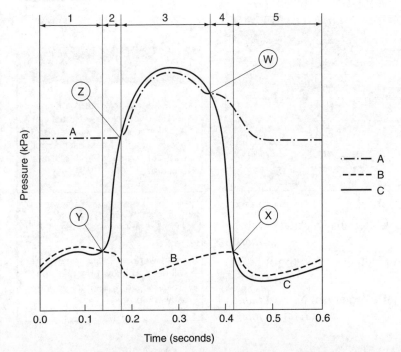

TUTORIAL TIP

Seemingly difficult, this part of the question is made easier if you remember the sequence of events in the cardiac cycle for the left side of the heart and the basic premise that blood will flow from a region of higher pressure to one of lower pressure.

(i)   Of the three lines A, B and C, state which represents pressure in the left atrium, in the left ventricle and in the aorta?   (*3 marks*)

(ii) Which one of the time periods 1–5 represents the emptying of the left ventricle?   (*1 mark*)

(iii) Which time periods 1–5 represent the filling of the left ventricle?   (*1 mark*)

(iv) At which of the points labelled W–Z on the graph do the valves between the left atrium and left ventricle (mitral / bicuspid valves) close?   (*1 mark*)

(v) At which of the points W–Z do the semi-lunar valves close?

          (*1 mark*)

          (*Total 16 marks*)

TUTORIAL TIP

Note the plural use of 'periods' in parts (iii) and (iv). Clearly more than one of the time periods 1–5 is needed in your response.

Q. 4

Study carefully the data given below for four different species of plants.

Plant species	A	B	C	D
Relative number of stomata mm^{-2} of leaf (upper:lower leaf surface)	5:30	0:80	10:15	0:50
Relative transpiration rate (upper:lower leaf surface)	10:12	0:4	15:30	20:50

(a)   Comment on the distribution of stomata in the four species. (*4 marks*)

(b)   Comment on the relationship between the distribution of the stomata and the transpiration rate in:
    (i)   species B, and   (*3 marks*)
    (ii) species D.   (*2 marks*)

(c)   From the data, what conclusions can be drawn about the differences between the upper leaf surfaces of species B and D?   (*2 marks*)

          (*Total 11 marks*)

TUTORIAL TIP

Make comparisons not only between the two surfaces of a single species but also between the different species – both in overall number and distribution.

Q. 5

The following table shows the relative concentration of urine in different mammals relative to the concentration in man (the value for man is taken as an arbitrary unit of 1.00). The corresponding thickness of the medulla (inner region) of the kidney is given for each mammal. The thickness is measured relative to the size of the remainder of the rest of the kidney.

Mammal	Urine concentration (relative to man)	Thickness of medulla (relative to remainder of kidney)
Man	1.00	3.0
Otter	0.35	1.1
Sheep	0.70	2.2
Rat	1.92	5.4
Gerbil	4.15	9.1
Organism X	3.73	8.9

(a)   Present these results as a suitable line graph.   (*3 marks*)

(b)   State the relationship between the relative medulla thickness and the urine concentration.   (*3 marks*)

(c)   Give a possible reason for the relationship you described in (b).   (*4 marks*)

(d)   Suggest, with reasons, the possible habitat of organism X.   (*4 marks*)

          (*Total 14 marks*)

TUTORIAL TIP

As neither set of data is an independent variable, the figures can be plotted either way around on the graph. Mark each point with the name of the relevant organism.

TUTORIAL TIP

To answer part (c) accurately you will need to know how nephrons are arranged within the kidney as a whole.

Q. 6

Read the following and then, using your knowledge, answer the questions that follow.

Since 1984, researchers have known that HIV enters cells using a protein called gp120. This molecule gets a grip on immune cells through a protein receptor on their surfaces called CD4. But not all cells carrying CD4 receptors are susceptible to HIV, so AIDS researchers reasoned that there must be at least one more receptor waiting to 5 be discovered.

This requirement for a 'co-receptor' also explains a puzzling transformation that HIV undergoes before it causes AIDS. While the infection is kept at bay and patients show no symptoms, viruses in their blood infect immune cells called macrophages and T cells. 10 But when the virus starts to win its struggle with the immune system, new variants appear that target only T cells.

Both macrophages and T cells carry CD4 receptors, so many researchers have argued that the change may be due to a switch in preference from one co-receptor to another. Biochemist Ed Berger and 15 his team succeeded where others have failed by working, not with HIV itself, but with mouse cells engineered to carry gp120 on their outer membranes. The researchers took a collection of human genes, inserted them individually into CD4 cells that were able to resist the virus, and mixed these cells with the mouse gp120 cells. 20

The scientists predicted that the CD4 cells that received a co-receptor gene would fuse with the gp120 mouse cells, creating a large and visible cell. To make these cells even easier to see, the researchers added one gene to the gp120 mouse cells and another to test CD4 cells which, if they both ended up in the same cell, produced 25 a substance that stained blue.

From the small numbers of large, blue cells produced in these experiments Berger's team retrieved a gene coding for a cell-surface protein that they have named fusin. When cells carrying neither CD4 nor fusin were given the genes for both, they became susceptible to 30 HIV.

One rapid payoff from the discovery may be the development of a simple animal model of AIDS. At present researchers can only study HIV infection in chimpanzees, or in mice whose immune system has been replaced with human cells. Berger's work shows that it should 35 be possible to make mice or rabbits succumb to HIV, by simply giving them the human genes for CD4 and fusin. He points out that transgenic animals carrying human CD4 already exist.

Berger's team have also found that the variants of HIV which target only T cells seem to bind particularly readily with fusin. This sug- 40 gests that the virus may indeed turn killer because it mutates to interact with fusin in preference to a still-undiscovered co-receptor found on the surface of macrophages. If so, drugs that stop this binding might slow the immune system damage that eventually kills people with AIDS. 'Now that we have the protein, we have a specific 45 target to develop drugs against', says Berger.

From an article by Philip Cohen in the *New Scientist*
No. 2030 (May 1996) entitled 'HIV Team Cracks Receptor Mystery'.

(a) Explain what is meant by the term 'transgenic animals' (line 38).

(2 marks)

(b) (i) What role do macrophages (line 10) play in the immune system?

(1 mark)

(ii) The T cells referred to in line 10, which are infected by HIV, are T-helper cells; what are the roles of these cells in the body's immune system? (*3 marks*)

(iii) Name the other two types of T cell in the human immune system and give the function of each. (*4 marks*)

(c) Give two disadvantages of the use of 'chimpanzees, or mice whose immune system has been replaced with human cells' (lines 34 to 35) for HIV research. (*2 marks*)

(d) What further information about the protein fusin would be necessary before drugs that bind to it are used on patients to control AIDS?

(*1 mark*)

(*Total 13 marks*)

Answers to practice questions on transport and exchange mechanisms

1.   (a) (i) A; (ii) B; (iii) E; (iv) D; (v) C.

(b) (i)   √ The data indicate that the rate of breathing is determined by the concentration of carbon dioxide in the inspired air (10% carbon dioxide – high rate; 0.04% carbon dioxide – much lower rate; 0% lower rate still),
√ because there is no logical relationship between the amount of oxygen and the breathing rate (100% oxygen – very low rate, 90% oxygen – very high rate, 80% oxygen – intermediate rate).
(ii) √ During mouth-to-mouth resuscitation expired air is forced into the patient's lungs. This expired air contains 4% carbon dioxide – 100 times more than in normal atmospheric air.
√ As we see from the graph an increase in the carbon dioxide concentration stimulates an increase in the breathing rate and will thus aid recovery.
√ Pressing the chest wall ventilates the lungs with air containing only 0.04% carbon dioxide and so is not as effective at stimulating the patient's respiratory rate, and recovery is therefore slower.

(c) √ The re-breathing of expired air leads to a progressive decrease in the concentration of oxygen and a progressive increase in the concentration of carbon dioxide.
√ The increase in carbon dioxide concentration will cause a rise in the rate of breathing.
√ The rise in breathing rate will compensate for the falling oxygen level and also act as a warning to the individual as it will cause some distress.
√ Soda lime absorbs carbon dioxide and so the breathing rate will not increase and may even fall slightly.
√ There will then be no compensatory increase in the amount of oxygen available in the lungs during a given time and no distress warning.
√ The oxygen level will continue to fall and the individual, being unaware of the danger may lapse into unconsciousness and death may follow.

(A maximum of 5 marks)

(d) √ Air contains around 20% oxygen and therefore the amount of oxygen available to the athlete at maximum air intake is $\frac{20}{5} = 4\,\text{dm}^3\,\text{min}^{-1}$.

√ The athlete uses $0.3\,dm^3$ oxygen each second and therefore in 1 minute uses $0.3 \times 60 = 18\,dm^3$.

√ With an oxygen debt of $14\,dm^3$ the total oxygen capacity for the first minute is $14\,dm^3 + 4\,dm^3 = 18\,dm^3$, and so the athlete can run for 1 minute before collapsing.

√ Running at $5\,m\,sec^{-1}$ the total distance that can be run in 1 minute is $5 \times 60 = \mathbf{300\,m}$

2. (a) The graph should look like this:

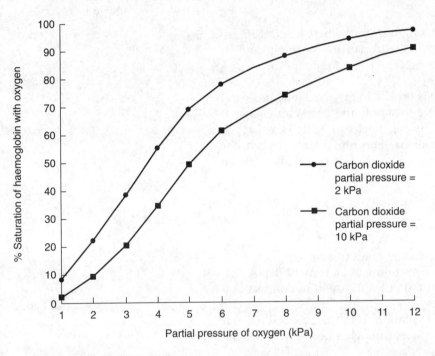

Marks are awarded for:
√ axes correct way round, labelled and units;
√ scale appropriate;
√ curves accurately plotted;
√ each curve correctly labelled and a title is provided for the graph.

(b) The effect of increasing carbon dioxide pressure is to:
√ reduce the ability of haemoglobin to take up oxygen
√ but thereby increase the ease with which oxygen is released from haemoglobin.

(c) (i) √ In the tissues especially actively respiring ones (i.e. where carbon dioxide is produced).
(ii) √ At the lung surface (i.e. where carbon dioxide is removed from the body).

(d) √ Where the partial pressure of carbon dioxide is low (i.e. the lungs) the haemoglobin of the red blood cells will more readily take up oxygen.
√ Where the partial pressure of carbon dioxide is high (i.e. in respiring tissues such as muscle or liver) the haemoglobin will more readily release its oxygen.

(e) (i) √ To the left
√ because it stores oxygen in muscle and so must have a greater affinity for it than haemoglobin if it is to load itself with oxygen brought to it in the bloodstream.

(ii)   √ To the left

√   because foetal haemoglobin needs to attract oxygen from the maternal haemoglobin at the placenta, if the foetus is to survive.

(iii)   √ To the right

√   because a mouse has a large surface to volume ratio and therefore has a high metabolic rate in order to maintain a constant temperature. It therefore needs its haemoglobin to release oxygen easily at the tissues and as the air it breathes is rich in oxygen it is still taken up readily in the lungs by haemoglobin despite its lowered affinity for it.

(iv)   √ To the left

√   because the llama lives at high altitude where reduced atmospheric pressure makes it difficult to load haemoglobin and its increased affinity for oxygen helps to compensate for this.

(v)   √ To the right

√   because flight in the pigeon is a highly energetic process it requires a high metabolic rate to supply the necessary energy. It is therefore important for its haemoglobin to release oxygen quickly at the tissues and as air contains much more oxygen, the lower affinity of haemoglobin for oxygen, is no disadvantage in picking it up in the lungs.

3.   (a)   (i)   √ D; (ii) √ B; (iii) √ A.

(b)   (i)   √ X = sino-atrial node (SAN);
√ Y = atrio-ventricular node (AVN);
√ Z = bundle of His / Purkinje fibres (tissue).

(ii)   √ X initiates heartbeat by sending out a wave of depolarisation / excitation across both atria causing them to contract and acts as the heart's pacemaker.

√   Y picks up the wave of excitation from the SAN and relays it after a short delay to the ventricles through a new wave of excitation / depolarisation.

√   Z transmits the wave of depolarisation / excitation from the AVN to the apex / base of the ventricles thus causing them to contract from the apex upwards.

(c)   (i)   √ A – pressure in the aorta;
√ B – pressure in the left atrium;
√ C – pressure in the left ventricle.

(ii)   √ Period 3 – when pressure in the left ventricle exceeds that in the aorta.

(iii)   √ Periods 1 and 5 (when the pressure in the left atrium exceeds that of the left ventricle).

(iv)   √ Point Y (the point when the atrial pressure first falls below that of the ventricle – thus preventing blood flowing back into the atrium).

(v)   √ Point W (the point when the ventricular pressure first falls below that of the aorta – thus preventing blood flowing back into the ventricle).

4.   (a)   √ In species A there are stomata on the upper surface, although the density is low, while the density on the lower surface is (*six times) greater.

√   In species B stomata are confined to the lower surface, only with a much greater density than in all other species (*at least 60% more).

√   In species C stomata are fairly evenly distributed between upper and lower surfaces (*half as many again on the lower surface). Compared with the other species there are less stomata overall, with fewer stomata than any other species on the lower surface but more on the upper.

√ In species D, stomata are confined to the lower surface, where they are more densely packed than in any other plant except species B.

√ *(BONUS) any relevant and accurate quantitative comparison – those shown are examples only.

(b) (i) √ Species B has the highest density of stomata overall, all of which are confined to the lower surface, and yet has the lowest transpiration rate.

√ This is unusual given that water loss predominantly occurs through stomata.

√ This suggests some xerophytic adaptations of the leaf, e.g. stomata in pits/grooves surrounded by hairs / closure at times of high transpiration.

(ii) √ The relatively high transpiration losses from the lower surface are expected due to the large number of stomata present.

√ The rate of loss from the upper surface is the greatest of all four species. Given that there are no stomata on this surface, all the water loss must be through the cuticle.

(c) √ Species B is likely to have a thick waxy cuticle preventing water loss

√ while species D has a very thin cuticle or possibly none at all.

5. (a)

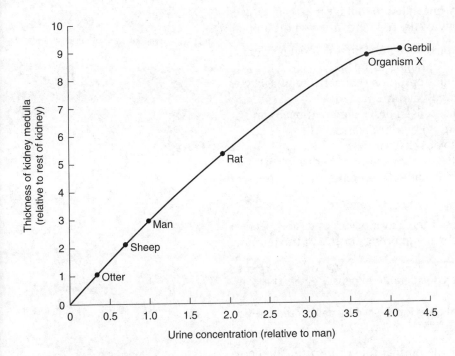

Marks awarded for:

√ axes suitable, correctly labelled;

√ scale appropriate and title given;

√ plots accurate and points labelled.

(b) √ There is almost a **direct** relationship between the thickness of the kidney medulla and the concentration of urine produced,

√ such that for a given increase in medulla thickness there is a similar increase in urine concentration.

√ In reality, the urine becomes slightly more concentrated for a given increase in medulla thickness and so the graph is slightly curved rather than a straight line.

(c) √ The medulla of the kidney is made up of the loops of Henle which are in the nephrons.

√ The longer the loops of Henle the thicker is the medulla.

√ The loops of Henle along with the collecting ducts form a counter-current system that helps to concentrate the urine and so conserve water.

√ The longer the loops of Henle (and hence the thickness of the medulla) the more water is conserved by the organism.

(d) √ Organism X most probably lives in a habitat where water conservation is essential.

√ As almost all mammals are terrestrial this is likely to be a hot arid place such as a hot desert.

√ This is likely as the kidney medulla of organism X is relatively thick and hence its urine is highly concentrated.

√ Its position on the graph lies close to that of the gerbil – an organism that lives in a hot desert where water conservation is paramount.

6. (a) √ Transgenic animals are ones that have had DNA from another organism introduced into their genome.

√ The 'foreign' DNA is stably integrated so that it can pass from generation to generation in effect giving rise to a new variety of the animal.

(b) (i) √ Macrophages are phagocytic and ingest foreign material including micro-organisms throughout the body.

(ii) √ T-helper cells produce opsonins that activate phagocytes such as macrophages to engulf harmful material.

√ They also assist T-killer cells in destroying pathogens and

√ activate B-lymphocytes to produce plasma cells.

(iii) √ T-killer cells (cytotoxic cells) that

√ kill any body cell that has become invaded by viruses by causing it to burst when cylindrical proteins rupture the cell membrane.

√ T-suppressor cells that

√ suppress the activities of the lymphocytes once an infection has been eliminated thereby maintaining control of the immune system.

(c) √ Any reference to the considerable expense, given the complexity of the process.

√ Any reference to the ethical questions raised by deliberately infecting animals with a deadly virus.

(d) √ An understanding of the normal role of fusin in the body, otherwise binding drugs to it might interfere with other systems causing unpleasant side-effects.

7 COORDINATION, RESPONSE AND CONTROL

Homeostasis

General principle

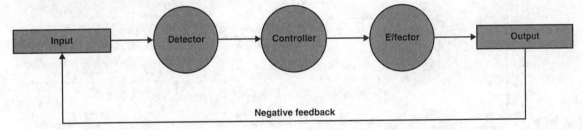

Input → Detector → Controller → Effector → Output

Negative feedback

Cellular homeostasis

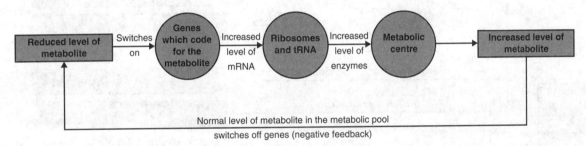

Reduced level of metabolite → Switches on → Genes which code for the metabolite → Increased level of mRNA → Ribosomes and tRNA → Increased level of enzymes → Metabolic centre → Increased level of metabolite

Normal level of metabolite in the metabolic pool switches off genes (negative feedback)

Body temperature homeostasis

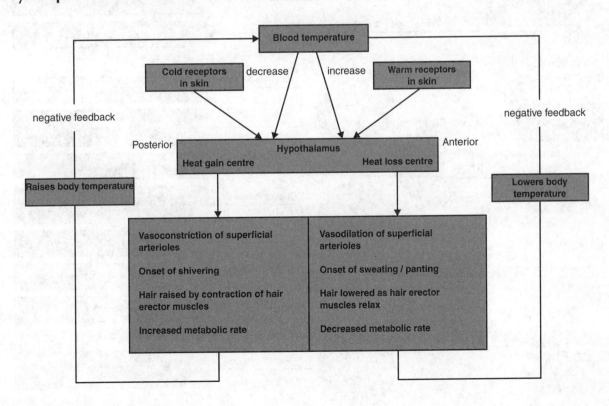

Blood temperature

Cold receptors in skin — decrease — increase — Warm receptors in skin

negative feedback — negative feedback

Posterior — Hypothalamus — Anterior

Heat gain centre — Heat loss centre

Raises body temperature — Lowers body temperature

Vasoconstriction of superficial arterioles

Onset of shivering

Hair raised by contraction of hair erector muscles

Increased metabolic rate

Vasodilation of superficial arterioles

Onset of sweating / panting

Hair lowered as hair erector muscles relax

Decreased metabolic rate

The endocrine system

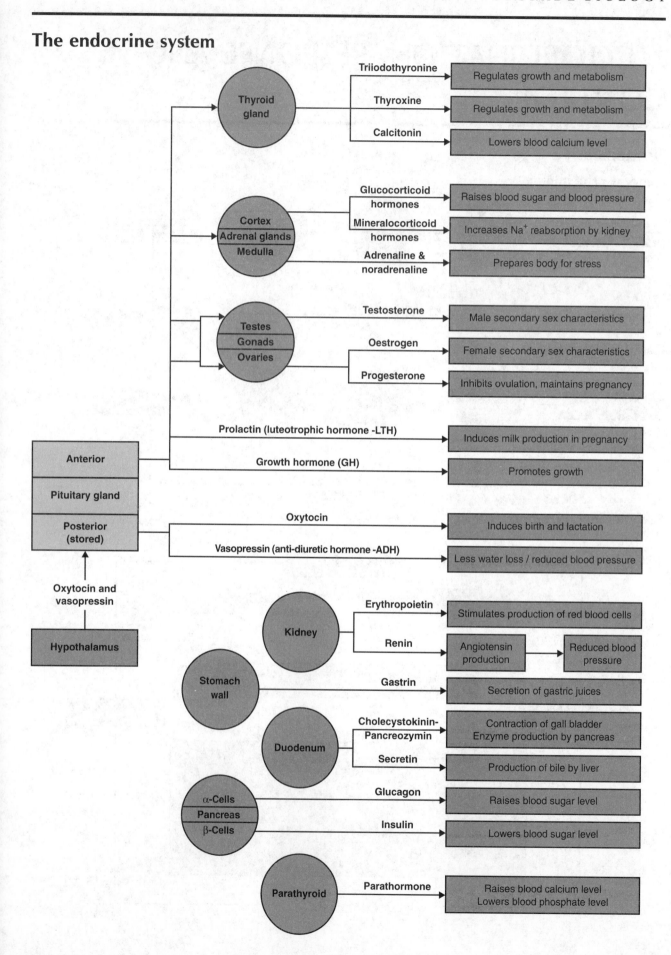

Autonomic nervous system

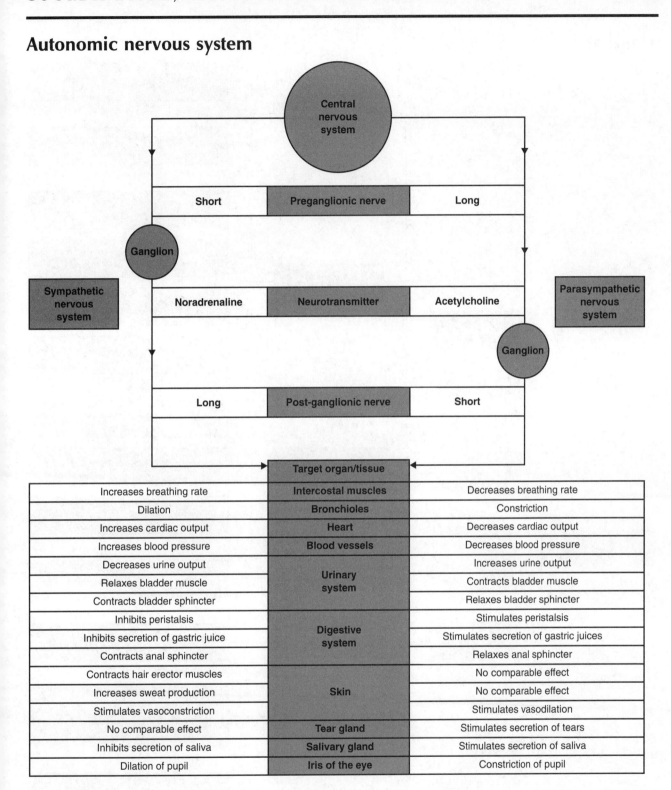

	Central nervous system	

Short	Preganglionic nerve	Long

Ganglion

Sympathetic nervous system

Noradrenaline	Neurotransmitter	Acetylcholine

Parasympathetic nervous system

Ganglion

Long	Post-ganglionic nerve	Short

	Target organ/tissue	
Increases breathing rate	Intercostal muscles	Decreases breathing rate
Dilation	Bronchioles	Constriction
Increases cardiac output	Heart	Decreases cardiac output
Increases blood pressure	Blood vessels	Decreases blood pressure
Decreases urine output	Urinary system	Increases urine output
Relaxes bladder muscle		Contracts bladder muscle
Contracts bladder sphincter		Relaxes bladder sphincter
Inhibits peristalsis	Digestive system	Stimulates peristalsis
Inhibits secretion of gastric juice		Stimulates secretion of gastric juices
Contracts anal sphincter		Relaxes anal sphincter
Contracts hair erector muscles	Skin	No comparable effect
Increases sweat production		No comparable effect
Stimulates vasoconstriction		Stimulates vasodilation
No comparable effect	Tear gland	Stimulates secretion of tears
Inhibits secretion of saliva	Salivary gland	Stimulates secretion of saliva
Dilation of pupil	Iris of the eye	Constriction of pupil

The brain

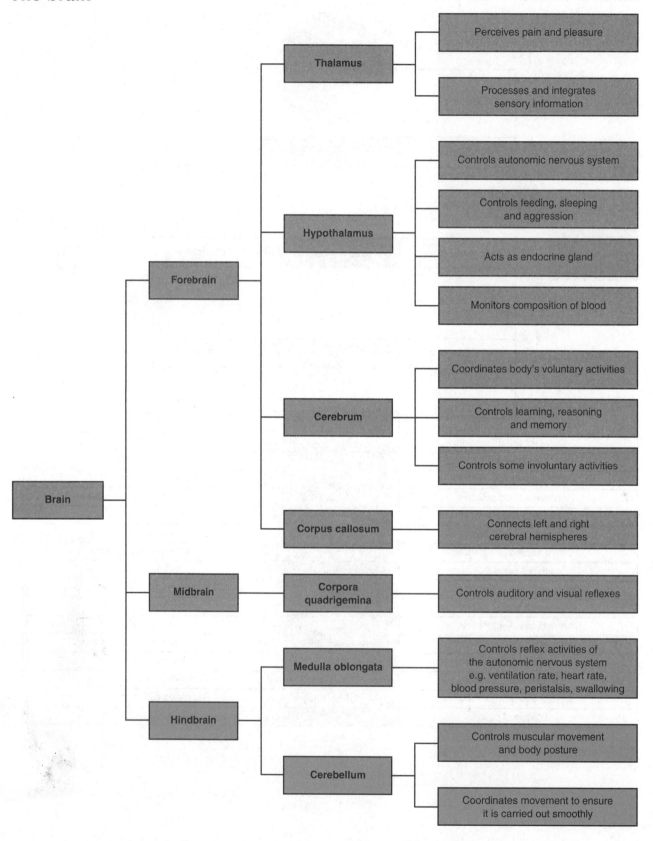

The mammalian eye

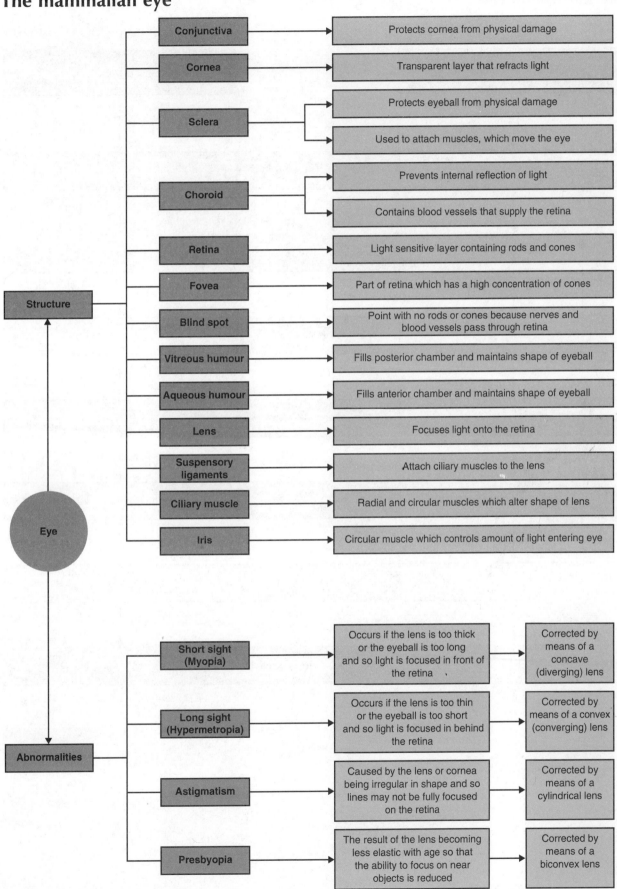

Structure

- **Conjunctiva** → Protects cornea from physical damage
- **Cornea** → Transparent layer that refracts light
- **Sclera** →
  - Protects eyeball from physical damage
  - Used to attach muscles, which move the eye
- **Choroid** →
  - Prevents internal reflection of light
  - Contains blood vessels that supply the retina
- **Retina** → Light sensitive layer containing rods and cones
- **Fovea** → Part of retina which has a high concentration of cones
- **Blind spot** → Point with no rods or cones because nerves and blood vessels pass through retina
- **Vitreous humour** → Fills posterior chamber and maintains shape of eyeball
- **Aqueous humour** → Fills anterior chamber and maintains shape of eyeball
- **Lens** → Focuses light onto the retina
- **Suspensory ligaments** → Attach ciliary muscles to the lens
- **Ciliary muscle** → Radial and circular muscles which alter shape of lens
- **Iris** → Circular muscle which controls amount of light entering eye

Eye

Abnormalities

- **Short sight (Myopia)** → Occurs if the lens is too thick or the eyeball is too long and so light is focused in front of the retina → Corrected by means of a concave (diverging) lens
- **Long sight (Hypermetropia)** → Occurs if the lens is too thin or the eyeball is too short and so light is focused in behind the retina → Corrected by means of a convex (converging) lens
- **Astigmatism** → Caused by the lens or cornea being irregular in shape and so lines may not be fully focused on the retina → Corrected by means of a cylindrical lens
- **Presbyopia** → The result of the lens becoming less elastic with age so that the ability to focus on near objects is reduced → Corrected by means of a biconvex lens

Accommodation (focusing) of objects by the eye

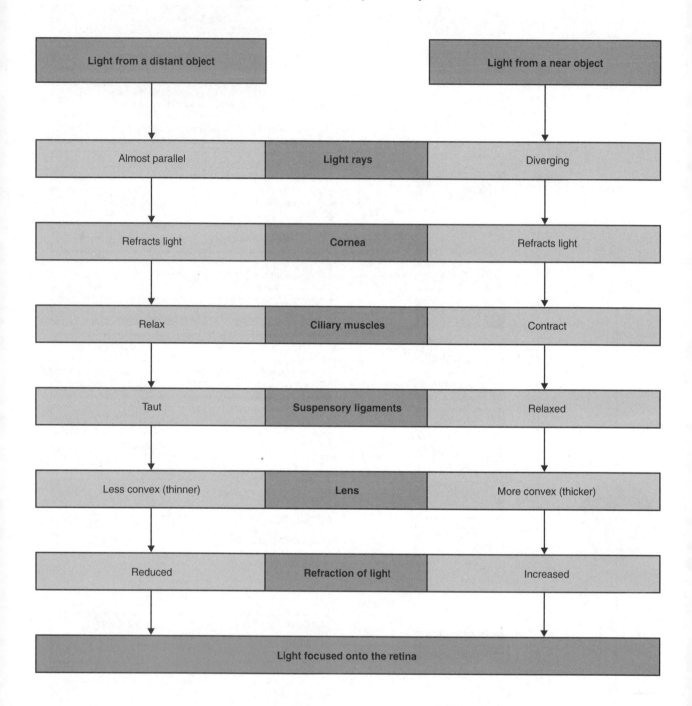

Light from a distant object		**Light from a near object**
Almost parallel	**Light rays**	Diverging
Refracts light	**Cornea**	Refracts light
Relax	**Ciliary muscles**	Contract
Taut	**Suspensory ligaments**	Relaxed
Less convex (thinner)	**Lens**	More convex (thicker)
Reduced	**Refraction of light**	Increased

Light focused onto the retina

Control of light entering the eye

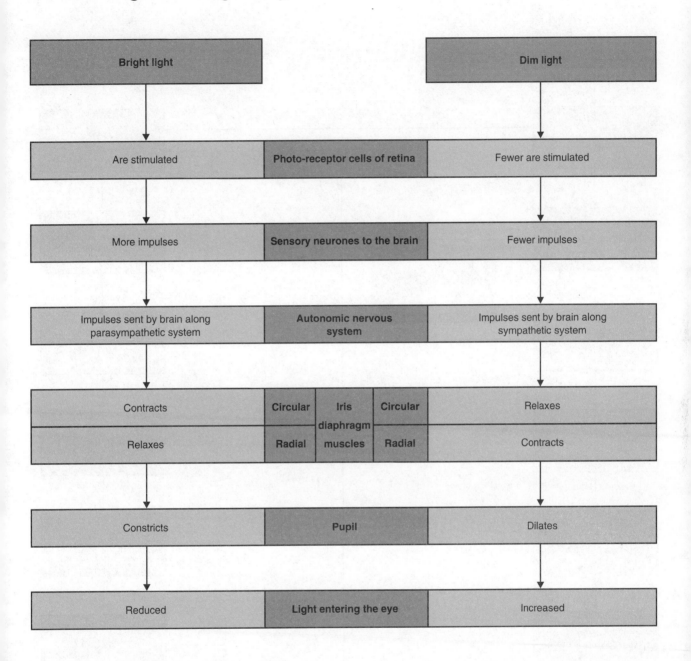

Muscle contraction

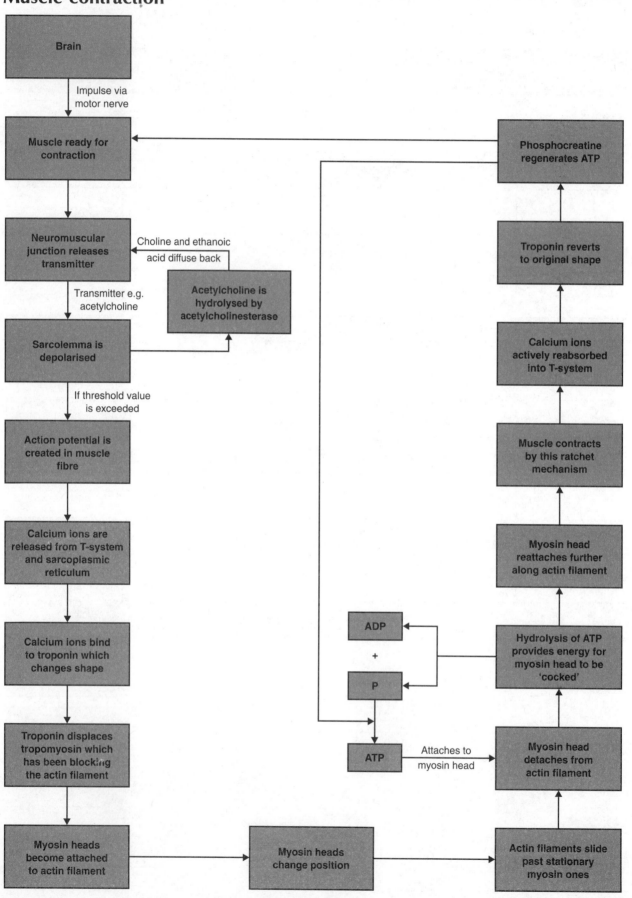

Plant hormones

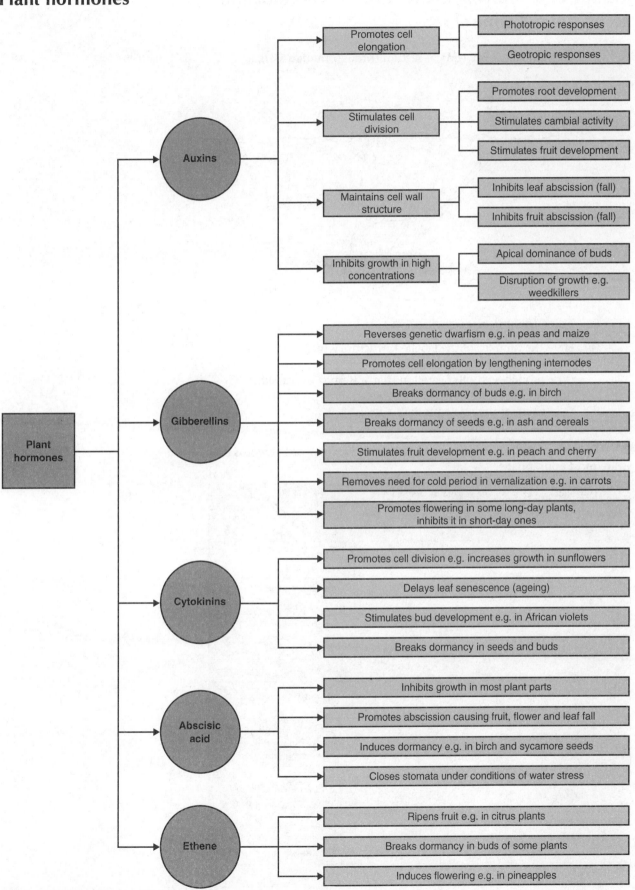

Testing and applying knowledge on coordination, response and control

1. The diagram below is a vertical section through human skin.

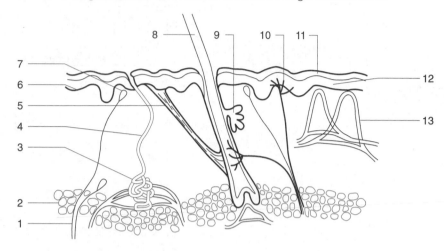

(a) Name the structures labelled 1–13.

(b) State the number of the labelled structure which:
   (i) contains the pigment melanin;
   (ii) produces an oily secretion that waterproofs the skin;
   (iii) acts as a long-term food reserve;
   (iv) excretes the waste product – urea.

2. For each of the numbers in the table below give the word or words that is/are most appropriate:

Hormone	Gland/organ producing the hormone	Function of the hormone
Thyroxine	Thyroid	1
2	3	Induces growth of facial hair in males
4	Stomach wall	Stimulates production of pepsin
5	Pancreas (β-cells)	6
Oxytocin	7	8
9	10	Increases rate of heartbeat
Thyroid stimulating hormone	11	12
13	Kidney	Stimulates production of angiotensin
Calcitonin	14	15
16	17	Alters permeability of kidney collecting ducts
18	Ovary	Inhibits production of follicle stimulating hormone by the pituitary
Aldosterone	19	20

3.   The diagram below shows the changes in potential difference across a nerve fibre membrane as an action potential passes along it.

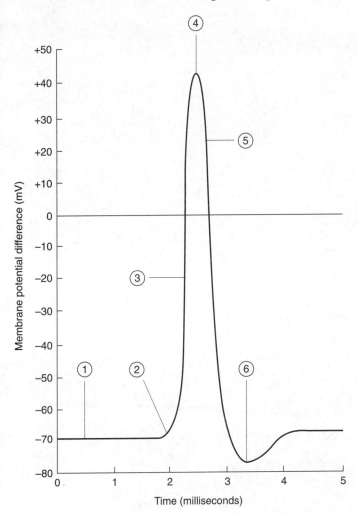

(a)   Which number on the diagram corresponds to each of the following statements (any number may be used once, more than once, or not at all).

(i)   There is a **rapid** movement of sodium ions into the axon.

(ii)   There is a rapid movement of potassium ions out of the axon.

(iii)   The outside of the axon membrane is **negatively** charged and there is no net movement of ions across it.

(iv)   The outside of the axon membrane is **positively** charged and there is no net movement of ions across it.

(v)   The axon is at resting potential.

(vi)   The relative refractory period.

(b)   By what means do sodium ions move across the axon membrane?

(c)   State **two** factors that are important in determining the speed of transmission of a nerve impulse and how each affects the speed.

4.   The diagram below shows part of a single myofibril from a striated muscle fibre. Below it is the same pattern shown in greater detail.

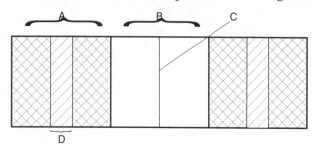

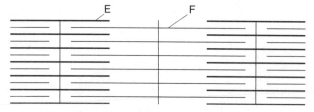

(a)   Give the names of the structures labelled A–F.

(b)   If the diagram shown is of a relaxed muscle, which of the labelled structures would be shorter when the muscle was contracted?

(c)   (i)   What structure attaches muscle to bone?
       (ii)   What type of protein fibre largely makes up this structure?
       (iii) Give **two** features of this fibre that suit it to this function.

5.   (a)   What term is used to describe each of the following responses:
       (i)   The movement of a maize stem towards a light source?
       (ii)   The growth of the root tip of a pea plant towards an area of moist soil?
       (iii) The movement of maggots away from a heat source?
       (iv)   Growth of a pollen tube towards chemicals produced by the micropyle?
       (v)   The swimming of the antherozoids (sperm) of a moss towards an archegonium (female structure) of another moss?
       (vi)   The movement of woodlice towards darker regions?
       (vii) The wrapping around a support of the petiole of a clematis leaf.

(b)   Give the names of the five groups of plant hormones.

(c)   State **four** differences between the structure and mode of action of plant hormones and animal hormones.

Answers to testing and applying knowledge on coordination response and control

1.   (a)   1 = Nerve fibre   2 = Adipose (fat) tissue
             3 = Sweat gland   4 = Sweat duct
             5 = Hair erector muscle   6 = Malpighian layer
             7 = (Touch/temperature) receptor   8 = Hair
             9 = Sebaceous gland   10 = Pain receptor
             11 = Stratum corneum   12 = Stratum granulosum
                  (cornified layer)   (granular layer)
             13 = Capillary plexus (network)/arteriole

(b)   (i) 6; (ii) 9; (iii) 2; (iv) 3.

2.   1 = Regulates growth and development of cells
2 = Testosterone
3 = Testis
4 = Gastrin
5 = Insulin
6 = Decreases blood sugar level
7 = Hypothalamus (via posterior pituitary)
8 = Induces birth and lactation
9 = Adrenaline
10 = Adrenal medulla
11 = Anterior pituitary
12 = Stimulates thyroid gland to produce thyroxine
13 = Renin
14 = Thyroid
15 = Lowers blood calcium level
16 = Anti-diuretic hormone (vasopressin)
17 = Hypothalamus (via posterior pituitary)
18 = Progesterone
19 = Adrenal cortex
20 = Increases retention of sodium ions by the kidney

3.   (a) (i) 3; (ii) 5; (iii) 4; (iv) 1; (v) 1; (vi) 6.

(b) Diffusion along a concentration gradient when the channel/gates are open.

(c) Diameter of the axon – the larger the diameter the faster the speed of transmission.
The presence of a myelin sheath – myelinated neurones conduct impulses faster than unmyelinated ones.

4.   (a) A = Anisotropic band; B = Isotropic band;   C = Z-line;
          D = H-zone;   E = Myosin filament; F = Actin filament;

(b) Structures B and D

(c) (i)   Tendon (white fibrous tissue)
(ii)   Collagen
(iii) It is very strong, being able to withstand tensions of up to $120 \, kg \, cm^{-2}$ without breaking. It is inelastic, and so contractions of the muscle result in movement of the bone rather than stretching of the tendon.

5.   (a) (i)   Positive phototropism
(ii)   Positive hydrotropism
(iii) Negative thermotaxis
(iv)   Positive chemotropism
(v)   Positive chemotaxis
(vi)   Negative phototaxis
(vii) Positive thigmotropism

(b) Auxins, gibberellins, cytokinins, abscisic acid and ethene.

(c)

Plant hormones	Animal hormones
No special sites for their synthesis, although it is normally restricted to specific regions.	Secreted by discrete specialised glands.
Transported largely by diffusion with some transport via phloem.	Transported in the blood that is pumped around the body by the heart.
Transport and action is slow.	Transport and action is mostly relatively rapid.
Chemically they are indole or purine based.	Chemically they are mostly steroids or polypeptides.

Sample question on coordination, response and control

In an experiment, the same quantity of the hormone gibberellin was applied to either the first leaf or the stem of dwarf bean plants and the leaf area of the plants was then measured over the following 3 weeks.

The experiment was then repeated under exactly the same conditions except that the tip of each plant was removed at the same time that the gibberellin was added. The control experiment in both cases was to use a group of plants to which no gibberellin was added. The results are shown in the graphs below:

(a) Tips of bean plants left intact

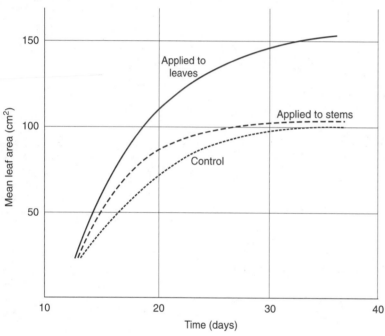

(b) Tips of bean plants removed

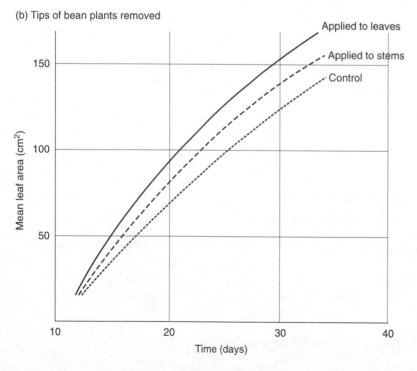

(a)   (i)   Using evidence from the graphs state what effects the removal of
            the growing tip has on the growth of the leaves in the absence of gib-
            berellin.   (3 marks)
      (ii) From your knowledge of plant hormones in general, give a possi-
            ble reason for these effects.   (1 mark)

(b)   What differences occur when gibberellin is applied to the leaves rather
      than the stem of intact bean plants?   (4 marks)

(c)   (i)   In what ways did the removal of the growing tips influence leaf
            size when gibberellin was applied?   (5 marks)
      (ii) Put forward a hypothesis that could explain these influences.
                                                                        (3 marks)

(d)   At a cellular level, how might an increase in leaf area occur?
                                                                        (2 marks)
                                                                  (Total 18 marks)

Guided response to sample question on coordination, response and control

(a)   (i)   In the absence of the growing tip the control experiment (dotted)
            line rises more steeply, reaches a higher point after 35 days and does
            not reach a plateau. These three observations lead to the following
            three conclusions. The removal of the growing tip causes:

            √ slower / less leaf growth / expansion over the initial period of the
            experiment (approximately $60\,cm^2$ leaf area after 20 days compared
            with $70\,cm^2$ when the tip remains intact);

            √ more overall leaf growth / expansion over the period of the experi-
            ment (approximately $140\,cm^2$ leaf area compared with $100\,cm^2$ when
            the growing tip is intact);

            √ leaf growth / expansion continues rather than ceasing after 35 days
            as it does when the tip remains intact.

      (ii) It could be argued that the removal of the tip leaves more nutrients
            available for the rest of the plant, including the leaves, which therefore
            grow more rapidly but the phrase 'from your knowledge of plant hor-
            mones in general' suggests another reason is required, namely:

            √ auxins are produced in the growing tips and these inhibit / suppress
            leaf growth / expansion.

(b)   Again you need to observe three differences between the leaf (solid)
      line and the stem (broken) line, namely that for the leaf the final point of
      levelling off (plateau) is higher, the gradient is greater throughout and the
      line is still rising (albeit very slightly) at the end of the experiment.

      It is also necessary to note that the control (dotted) line and the stem
      (broken) line meet after approximately 32 days. From these observations
      you should conclude that when gibberellin is applied to the leaves rather
      than the stem then:

      √ the overall area of the leaves is greater ($150\,cm^2$ compared with $100\,cm^2$
      when applied to the stem);

      √ the **rate** of leaf growth / expansion is greater;

      √ leaf growth / expansion is still continuing after 35 days rather than reach-
      ing a maximum size after 32 days;

      √ the final leaf area is greater than when no gibberellin is applied (control)
      whereas it is the same if gibberellin is applied to the leaves.

TUTORIAL TIP

The control experiment is the one
that is carried out 'in the absence
of gibberellin', therefore compare
the two dotted lines.

TUTORIAL TIP

Use specific data from the graphs
to support your answers.

TUTORIAL TIP

If uncertain of exactly which hormone is involved you could
simply use the term hormone,
but the more precise your
answer is, the more credit is
likely to be awarded.

(c)   (i)   Here you need to compare the leaf (solid) lines and the stem (broken) lines on the two graphs. This comparison should lead you to state that when the growing point is removed:
√   the growth / expansion of the leaves is initially slower (up to 20–25 days);
√   the growth / expansion continued for longer;
√   the growth / expansion did not level off (plateau);
√   the final leaf area was greater;
√   the removal of the growing tip had a much more pronounced effect when gibberellin was applied to the stems than when it was applied to the leaves.
(ii)   Any reasonable hypothesis is likely to bring credit, but the most probable one is:
√   auxins are made in the growing tips;
√   and these inhibit/suppress the effect of gibberellin overall;
√   and may increase the transport of gibberellins into the leaves from the stems.

(d)   There are two ways in which a group of cells might increase their area / volume:
√ by increasing their number through mitotic division;
√ by increasing the size of each cell through expansion / elongation as a result of the uptake of water / nutrients (or a combination of both!).

Practice questions on coordination, response and control

Q. 1

(a)   (i)   What is meant by the terms endothermy and ectothermy?
(2 marks)
(ii)   Give **two** advantages of endothermy and **two** advantages of ectothermy.
(4 marks)

(b)   What is the relationship between body size and heat regulation?
(2 marks)

(c)   (i)   Where in the brain is the centre that controls body temperature in mammals?
(1 mark)
(ii)   Explain how this temperature control centre produces an increase in the rate of sweating as a result of a rise in body temperature.
(4 marks)
(iii)   State **four** effects produced by the temperature control centre when the body temperature falls.
(4 marks)

(d)   Why is the body temperature of a human foetus normally 0.5°C higher than that of his/her mother?
(3 marks)
(Total 20 marks)

Q. 2

(a)   Give an account of how an action potential that arrives at the presynaptic membrane of a cholinergic synapse causes a new action potential to be generated in the postsynaptic neurone.
(7 marks)

(b) Using your knowledge of a human's nervous and endocrine systems, explain each of the following as fully as you can:

(i) Drugs such as atropine, which inhibit the parasympathetic nervous system, may produce side-effects such as blurred vision and a dry mouth. *(2 marks)*

(ii) Nicotine in tobacco smoke increases blood pressure. *(2 marks)*

(iii) Strychnine is a lethal chemical that inhibits the breakdown of acetylcholine. *(2 marks)*

(iv) Local anaesthetics may contain noradrenaline. *(2 marks)*

(v) Contraceptive pills contain oestrogen and progesterone. *(2 marks)*

(vi) The addition of iodine to salt may prevent goitre. *(2 marks)*

(vii) Diabetics must inject insulin rather than taking it orally. *(1 mark)*

(Total 20 marks)

Q. 3
The number of cells in the human retina was determined along a horizontal line from the nose side of the eye to the outer side. The results are shown in the graphs below.

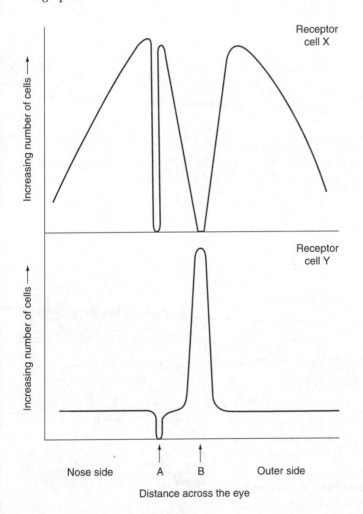

(a) Name the receptor cells X and Y. *(2 marks)*

(b) (i) Why are both types of receptor cell absent at point A? *(2 marks)*

(ii) What name is given to point A? *(1 mark)*

(c) (i)   Explain the distribution of receptor cells at point B.   *(4 marks)*
     (ii) What name is given to point B.   *(1 mark)*
     (iii) Explain why it may be easier to see a dimly lit object by looking
     slightly to one side of it.   *(3 marks)*

(d) (i)   Why do objects that are coloured in bright light only appear in
     black and white when light intensity is low?   *(4 marks)*
     (ii) Explain why on entering a dimly lit room from bright surround-
     ings, objects only gradually become visible.   *(3 marks)*

                                                                  (Total 20 marks)

TUTORIAL TIP

Remember to explain the distribution of **both** cells X and Y, not
just Y.

Q. 4

The figure below represents a human leg with only its femur bone shown in
detail. The associated muscles are represented by a letter in a box and its
points of attachment represented by arrows leading from each box.

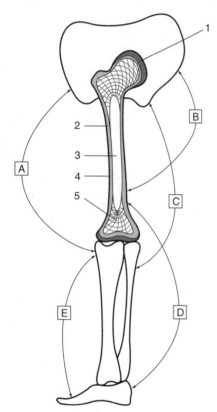

(a)   Name the structures labelled 1–5.   *(5 marks)*

(b) (i)   What name is given to the structures that connect bone to bone?
                                                                       (1 mark)
     (ii) What properties of this structure suit it to its function. *(2 marks)*

(c)   Giving reasons for your answers, indicate by appropriate letters which
muscle or muscles are contracted when the following actions are carried out:
     (i)   The toes are lifted with the heel on the ground.   *(2 marks)*
     (ii) The knee is lifted with the toes pointing downwards.   *(2 marks)*
     (iii) The heel is raised behind the knee with the foot hanging loose.
                                                                       (2 marks)
                                                                  (Total 14 marks)

TUTORIAL TIP

Bear in mind that the contraction
of any muscle will cause movement of the lower bone to
which it is attached as well as all
other bones below it.

TUTORIAL TIP

All muscles behind the limb will
move the relevant part of the
leg backwards, those in front of
the limb will move it forwards.

Q. 5

Read the following and then, using your knowledge, answer the questions that follow.

The explosive pace of scientific discovery in the biological arena continues to uncover an increasing array of proteins of immense potential therapeutic importance. Many of these proteins, which need to be extensively purified before use, are now entering clinical trials. Even if they prove successful in the trials, they are 5 unlikely to gain marketing approval until well into the next century. Arguably the most exciting family of potential therapeutic agents are the neurotrophic factors. This is a family of small (average molecular weight 13 000 Daltons) proteins, containing an unusually high proportion of basic amino acids. They, along with 10 certain other growth factors, are essential for the development and survival of specific nerve cells (neurones) in both the central and peripheral nervous system.

The first neurotrophic factor to be discovered was nerve growth factor (NGF), which is essential for the development and maintenance 15 of a subset of sensory neurones, the sympathetic neurones as well as cholinergic basal forebrain neurones. NGF and other neurotrophic factors maintain several neuronal types, depletion of which is characteristic of several common neurodegenerative diseases.

Peripheral neuropathy, for example, is a condition often asso- 20 ciated with diabetes and leads to degeneration of certain sensory and motor neurones. Clinical consequences include ulceration of the extremities which contributes to tissue necrosis, often necessitating amputation of toes or feet. Nerve growth factor, along with another growth factor, insulin-like growth factor I, 25 are known to prevent drug-induced peripheral neuropathy. For this reason clinical trials assessing their effectiveness in treating diabetes-associated neuropathies have begun.

Neurotrophic factors may also prove useful in the treatment of certain neurodegenerative diseases of the brain, such as Alzhei- 30 mer's and Parkinson's disease, for which no effective therapeutic agents are currently available. Alzheimer's, for example, is characterised by the destruction of cholinergic neurones in the forebrain, associated with the hippocampus, which appear to mediate the memory process. NGF has been shown to support the growth of these 35 neurones *in vitro* and may therefore be capable of arresting their degeneration in Alzheimer's patients.

While the therapeutic potential of neurotrophic factors should not be underestimated, initial clinical trials using individual neurotrophic factors have in some cases proved disappointing. How- 40 ever, recent research findings suggest that optimal beneficial effects may require a combination of such factors. Other technical difficulties also remain, not least of which is how to ensure efficient transport of these substances across the blood–brain barrier, a prerequisite for effective treatment of neurodegenera- 45 tive diseases of the brain.

From an article 'Biopharmaceuticals: Prospects for the Future'
by Gary Walsh in the *Journal of the Institute of Biology*, Vol. 43, No. 2.

(a) What is meant by the following terms?
    (i) 'therapeutic agents' (lines 7–8)   (*1 mark*)
    (ii) 'tissue necrosis' (line 23)   (*1 mark*)
    (iii) *'in vitro'* (line 36)   (*1 mark*)

(b)   Give **two** reasons why the proteins need to be 'extensively purified' (line 4) before being used in clinical trials.   (*2 marks*)

(c)   In the passage, three types of neurones are referred to, each of which is one of an alternative pairing. In each case describe the type of neurone and give its opposite type.

    (i)   'sensory neurones' (line 16)   (*2 marks*)
    (ii)   'sympathetic neurones' (line 16)   (*2 marks*)
    (iii) 'cholinergic neurones' (line 17)   (*2 marks*)
                                      (*Total 11 marks*)

Answers to practice questions on coordination, response and control

1.   (a)   (i)   √ In ectothermy the body temperature of animals fluctuates with that of the environment and they regulate their body temperature by behavioural means.

        √ In endothermy the body temperature of animals is maintained at a constant level because they regulate it using metabolic and physiological as well as behavioural means.

        (ii)   √ **Endothermy** allows an animal to:

        √ be more independent of its environment and so have a wider geographical range;

        √ have a constant (and usually higher) metabolic rate so that enzymes operate at a more predictable, and often faster, level.

        √ **Ectothermy** allows an animal to:

        √ use less food / expend less energy;

        √ not require complex thermoregulatory systems.

    (b) √ Heat is lost / gained more readily when the surface area to volume ratio is large, and lost / gained less easily, where it is small.

    √ As larger animals have a smaller surface area to volume ratio they lose/gain heat less readily and so can regulate their body temperature better as they are subject to less severe fluctuations in temperature.

    (c)   (i)   √ Hypothalamus

        (ii) √ Receptors/sense cells in the hypothalamus detect a rise in temperature of the blood passing through it.

        √ The heat loss centre of the hypothalamus sends nerve impulses

        √ via the sympathetic/autonomic nervous system causing

        √ an increased blood flow to the sweat glands and hence an increase in sweat production.

        (iii) √√√√ Any four from:

- reduction in sweating;
- hair erection;
- shivering;
- vasoconstriction of surface blood vessels;
- increased metabolic rate.

    (d) √ The foetus produces much heat because it has a high rate of metabolism/respiration as a result of its rapid rate of growth.

    √ It is unable to lose this heat directly to its environment, but does so via the placenta.

    √ However, heat will only transfer to the mother's blood across the placenta along a temperature gradient and therefore the foetal blood must be at a higher temperature than the mother's for this to occur.

2. (a) √ Action potential arriving at the presynaptic membrane initiates an influx of calcium ions (Ca^{2+}),

√ which causes the synaptic vesicles to fuse with the membrane so releasing their neurotransmitter, acetylcholine, into the synaptic cleft.

√ The acetylcholine diffuses across the synaptic cleft and fuses with receptor molecules on the postsynaptic membrane.

√ As a result, ion channels on this membrane open and sodium ions rush in

√ creating an excitatory postsynaptic potential,

√ which will evoke a new action potential in the postsynaptic neurone provided it exceeds the threshold value.

√ The acetylcholine is broken down by the enzyme acetylcholinesterase on the postsynaptic membrane.

(b) (i) √ The parasympathetic system stimulates saliva production so when it is inhibited the mouth becomes dry.

√ The parasympathetic system also constricts the pupils of the eyes and so the drug leads to their dilation, giving blurred vision.

(ii) √ Nicotine stimulates the production of adrenaline by the adrenal glands.

√ Adrenaline increases the heart rate leading to a higher blood pressure.

(iii) √ The inhibition of the breakdown of acetylcholine means that this neurotransmitter causes continuous stimulation of the postsynaptic neurone,

√ which leads to overstimulation of vital body systems, e.g. heart and brain, leading to death.

(iv) √ Noradrenaline causes constriction of arterioles

√ and this keeps the effects of the anaesthetic localised by reducing the risk of blood flushing it away and affecting other parts of the body.

(v) √ If oestrogen and progesterone in the blood are maintained at a high level, the production of gonadotrophic hormones (e.g. luteinising hormone) from the pituitary gland is inhibited.

√ The absence of luteinising hormone stops ovulation and so prevents conception.

(vi) √ Goitre can be caused by the inability of the thyroid gland to produce sufficient thyroxine.

√ Each molecule of thyroxine has four atoms of iodine and therefore an adequate supply of iodine is needed in the diet to make thyroxine – iodised salt is one means of ensuring this supply.

(vii) √ Insulin is a polypeptide – taken orally it would be digested by pepsin in the stomach into its constituent peptides thus rendering it ineffective.

3. (a) √ X = Rod cells; √ Y = Cone cells

(b) (i) √ The neurones from all retinal cells pass over the inner surface of the eye in front of the cells themselves before converging to form the optic nerve,

√ which then passes through the retina, at which point there can be no receptor cells.

(ii) √ Blind spot

(c) (i) √ Point B lies on the optical axis directly opposite the centre of the lens.

√ It is at this point that the greatest concentration of light from an object falls when a person is looking directly at it.

√ As Y receptor cells (cones) are sensitive to bright light, their concentration is greatest at this point.

√ As X receptor cells (rods) are ineffective in bright light because they are overstimulated, none are found at this point.

(ii) √ Fovea centralis (yellow spot).

(iii) √ Low intensity (dim) light can only be detected by rod cells (cells X).

√ As light falls on the fovea (point B) when an object is viewed directly and there are no rod cells (cells X) at this point, it will not generate any action potentials, i.e. will be invisible.

√ By looking slightly to one side of the object, light will strike the retina to one side of the fovea (point B) where rod cells (cells X) are present and hence action potentials will be created in these and the object becomes visible.

(d) (i)   √ In bright light the cone cells (cells Y) are stimulated and these are of three types, each responding to a different wavelength (colour) of light: 430 nm (blue), 530 nm (green) and 570 nm (red).

√ Differential stimulation of all three provides the full range of colour vision.

√ In dim light only rod cells (cells X) are stimulated,

√ of which there is only one type, which is either stimulated (appears white) or not (appears black).

(ii) √ In bright surroundings the circular muscles of the iris diaphragm are contracted and the pupil of the eye is constricted to prevent too much light entering the eye and overstimulating the retinal cells.

√ On entering a dimly lit room the radial muscles of the iris contract and the pupil dilates,

√ but the process takes a little time during which there is insufficient light entering the eye to exceed the threshold value of the rod cells (cells X), which are the only ones that detect low intensity light, and so nothing is visible until dilation is complete.

4.   (a)   √ 1 – Cartilage   √ 2 – Compact (hard) bone
              √ 3 – Marrow cavity   √ 4 – Periosteum
              √ 5 – Spongy (cancellous) bone

(b) (i)   √ Ligaments

(ii) √ They have strength so that they can hold bones together against the pull of the muscles on them,

√ but are also elastic and flexible so that there can be movement about the joints.

(c) (i)   √ To lift the toes with the heel on the ground involves the distance between the toes and the tibia (front bone of lower leg) becoming shorter. To achieve this the muscle joining these two structures must contract.

√ This is muscle E.

(ii) √ To point the toes downwards the heel must be pulled upwards, which entails muscle D being contracted.

√ Raising the knee involves shortening the distance between the knee and the pelvic girdle, which entails muscle A being contracted.

(iii) √ If the heel is raised behind the knee, the leg must be flexed at the knee, which involves shortening the distance between the lower leg and the back of the pelvic girdle.

√ Contraction of muscle C will achieve this.

5.   (a)   (i)   √ Factors used in the treatment and cure of disease.

(ii)   √ The death of groups of cells as a result of disease or injury.

(iii)   √ Taking place outside the body in a test-tube, culture dish or other container (Latin – 'in glass').

(b)   √   Impurities may be dangerous to health of the patients / cause unpleasant side effects.

√   To judge the effectiveness of a specific protein, it must be used alone otherwise it is impossible to determine whether the effects are due to it, or one of the contaminants.

(c)   (i)   √ Neurones that carry nerve impulses from receptor cells to the central nervous system. Its opposite type are:

√   effector (motor) neurones.

(ii)   √ Sympathetic neurones ganglia (cell bodies and synapse) close to the central nervous system. They largely increase the rate of involuntary processes. Their opposing type are:

√   parasympathetic neurones.

(iii)   √ Cholinergic neurones use acetylcholine as a neurotransmitter. Their opposing type use noradrenaline and are therefore known as:

√   adrenergic neurones.

PART 3

GUIDANCE ON PRACTICAL AND PROJECT WORK

8 HOW TO PERFORM PRACTICAL WORK AND CARRY OUT PROJECTS

Although it's easy to feel that your trial A-level grade will depend on how well you answer structured or essay questions it is important to remember that your practical skills will also contribute substantially. This can be to your advantage because the practical work will form an integral part of your biology course and it will give you an opportunity to demonstrate some of your ability without the pressure and time limitation imposed by an examination. You may be expected to master the use of a microscope and produce drawings of biological specimens, and you will also have to carry out experiments or longer investigations.

Microscopy and drawing

All too often the problems students face with microscopy are simply due to the microscope being set up so badly that it cannot provide an adequate quality of image. If you encounter problems a run through this simple check list should sort out your difficulties.

- Are the lenses clean? – if not remove them carefully and wipe them with lens tissue.
- Is the objective lens 'clicked' into place?
- Is the diaphragm open?
- Is all the light falling below the stage? – loss of image quality will occur if light enters from the side or above; if you have a mirror use the plane side, not the concave.
- Is the condenser adjusted correctly? – this should allow even illumination of the whole field.
- Is the specimen in the centre of the stage?
- Have you focused the specimen on a low power before turning to a high power objective?

Having set up your microscope properly you will be able to see specimens clearly enough to make drawings of them. A low-power plan should indicate the main regions of each cell type but you shouldn't draw individual cells. High power drawings should show a few adjacent cells (usually three or four) in detail.

Both types of drawing will need to be provided with a scale to indicate the **actual** size of the specimen. In order to do this you will need an eyepiece graticule in the microscope and this must be calibrated using a special slide called a stage micrometer so that you can obtain a precise measurement for each division on the graticule.

Don't panic if you're not an artist, good biological drawings can still be constructed if you follow these guidelines:

- Use a good quality, sharp pencil that is not so soft that it smudges, or so hard that you can't rub it out; an HB is usually best.
- Draw on good quality plain paper.
- Choose a suitable scale so that the drawing, labels and annotations will fit comfortably on the page.

- Make large, clear line drawings without the use of ink or coloured pencils.
- Keep the drawing simple by providing only an outline of all the basic structures.
- Draw accurately and faithfully what can be seen. Never draw anything you cannot see even if it is expected to be present. Never copy from books.
- Draw individual parts of a specimen in strict proportion to each other.
- Provide suitable headings that clearly indicate the nature of the drawing. For microscope drawings the section (TS/LS, etc.) should be stated.
- State the magnification, scale or actual size of the specimen.
- Label fully all biological features keeping labels away from the diagram, and never label on the actual drawing.
- Avoid crossing label lines and if possible arrange labels vertically one beneath the other.
- Use annotations to indicate the functions of the labelled parts.
- Keep all drawings carefully for assessment.

Experimental work

For much of the experimental work you carry out you may be given verbal or written instructions by your teachers, however, for projects and longer investigations you will have to plan and carry out your own experiment.

Planning

This is one of the most important aspects of your investigation, because if it is done properly everything else will fall into place. Often the most difficult thing is to decide what you want to investigate. Have you already carried out any experiments that could be extended? Have you noticed any patterns of vegetation or animal distribution when doing fieldwork? What sort of problems have previous students investigated? Whatever you decide to look at should not be too complex. Often the simplest idea, thoroughly studied, will lead to the best results. Remember that you must state and attempt to control all the possible variables in your experiment except the one whose effects you are studying. This can be difficult in fieldwork but a lot can be achieved by careful selection of your sites. Once you have decided on the topic you will have to predict what will happen in your investigation and state it as a clear and testable hypothesis. This is where a sound knowledge of theoretical biology is important because you must be able to back up your predictions.

It will be important that your investigation generates quantitative data and is not merely descriptive because otherwise you will find it difficult to justify acceptance or rejection of your hypothesis and a poor grade may result. The next step will be to write down all the stages of your experimental procedure, step-by-step, taking care to include references to safety issues and maintaining a respect for living organisms and the environment where relevant. If your experiment is going to take place over the course of several days or even weeks it will be useful to write a diary for yourself so that you remember exactly what is to be done on each day. You will need to write a complete list of all the apparatus/equipment you require (don't forget the matches!) as well as the chemicals and other materials. It will be necessary to keep a copy for yourself as well as supplying one for your teacher or technician. These lists must be detailed – measuring cylinders come in various sizes – so be precise. How many do you need? What volume? Which day? And what about the solutions? What concentration? How much sucrose solution? When? Did you expect your yeast to arrive as a lump or did you think it would be a nice bubbly suspension? **You** may know what you need but make sure everyone else does too.

When you first try out your experiment you may find it difficult to get reliable results. Don't worry – a trial run is very important. Keep the results and all your notes and then amend your procedure and try again. Update your requirements list and remember to include enough for more than one run through.

Collection of results

Thorough planning should make this part of your investigation straightforward and enjoyable. Trial runs will have enabled you to get used to handling your apparatus and to have modified your method to minimise errors. You should have a good idea of how many readings you will need to make, and at what intervals. It is important to be accurate – don't round everything up to whole numbers. The temperature 28.6°C is not the same as that of 29°C. It is vital to make notes of any observations you make during the collection of your results because they may help you with your discussion. All your original records of the results will also be needed – it is not sufficient to have neat copies or summaries of them. Don't forget to repeat your experiment – twice if possible – to increase the reliability of your results. If any reading seems anomalous look for reasons at the time, again it will make your final analysis easier.

Displaying your results

Although your raw results must be included in the final account of your investigation they will not be sufficient alone. It is also essential to make tables that summarise the results so that the overall pattern they display can readily be seen. Examiners will also look for suitable graphs or bar charts that clearly communicate your results. Remember to apply the skills that you may have learnt for answering examination questions – always tabulate everything clearly using suitable units, label the axes on your graphs, plot accurately and clearly and identify the curves you have drawn.

Writing the method

You will already have a clear step-by-step account of your procedure in the plan you wrote before carrying out your investigation. However, this will need to be rewritten in continuous prose in the light of any modifications you made during the experiment. The reason for each modification will need to be explained as will the reasons for any controls you used. The most important thing to remember about writing the method is that anyone reading it should be able to follow the directions you give and carry out an experiment in **exactly** the same way as you. So think carefully before you write; asterisks referring to notes/comments elsewhere on the page are not acceptable and neither is it reasonable to write '... but before *x* I did *y*' – by then the person following your instructions would have gone wrong!

Concluding and interpreting

If you have carried out your experiment carefully you should have recorded enough results to enable you to accept or reject your hypothesis. Your own subjective view of the significance of your results is not enough. You should apply a statistical test of significance, such as a χ^2 test or t-test, to them. Make sure you understand what the results of your statistical test mean – all too often students collect excellent results, do all the maths correctly and then completely misinterpret the value they read from the tables. Hopefully your results will demonstrate definite trends that you will be able to discuss and interpret with knowledge gained from your study of theoretical biology. Point out any results that do not fit the trend and attempt to account for them. At this point any notes you took during the course of your investigation might be helpful. Suggest what effect possible errors in your experiment might have had and consider how they might be overcome. Be sensible here – you are not going to be given credit for things that definitely should have been controlled, or careless errors like reading a thermometer incorrectly. A good discussion will always consider the biological importance of any findings and will refer to other relevant published work. So use your study skills to find references to material in journals and textbooks or on CD-ROM. If you have investigated a food product, disinfectant, toothpaste or any other consumer product write to the relevant companies, they will often provide you with useful background material. But, remember to do this in plenty of time, commercial enterprises will not always reply by return of post!

Presentation

Although you are unlikely to get extra marks just because your final account looks nice, it is a pity to spoil an investigation by careless presentation, which can lead to errors. It is just as acceptable to write as it is to word-process your material and examiners will not be fooled into thinking that a poor project is a good one just because a computer has been used. Which-ever technique you apply do not copy out your plan or raw results, they should always be submitted in their original form. Published scientific papers conform to a particular style that you may find useful to adopt for your investigation. They begin with a short account of the hypothesis being tested, methods used and overall conclusions. This is called an **abstract** and it allows other scientists to scan the main findings of the work quickly and to decide whether or not they would find it useful to read the whole account. This is followed by a brief **introduction,** which explains the hypothesis and refers to other similar experiments or work that may have been carried out. The next section will be more familiar to you : a **method** written in continuous prose, a summary of the **results**, a **discussion** of their significance and finally a **bibliography** quoting all the books or journals that have been used in the study. You will notice that this does not seem to leave a place for your plan, raw results, statistical test or relevant background material. All these should be placed at the back of your account in an **appendix** and referred to at relevant points in the discussion.

If you follow this format for the presentation of your investigation you will have a logical and impressive account with no omissions.